DINOFLAGELLATES
of the Caribbean Sea
and Adjacent Areas

DINOFLAGELLATES

of the Caribbean Sea

and Adjacent Areas

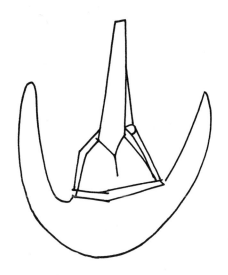

By E. J. FERGUSON WOOD

UNIVERSITY OF MIAMI PRESS
Coral Gables, Florida

CONTENTS

PREFACE

The studies presented in this monograph were undertaken to provide students with an atlas of the species of dinoflagellates with which they should be familiar in any study of the Caribbean region. Because of the differences of opinion regarding the validity of certain species and genera, and regarding some of the main taxonomic divisions, I have treated the genera of the dinoflagellates in alphabetical order.

The first section contains an illustrated glossary of the terms used and the characters required for determination of the genera and species. This is followed by a key to the genera. The major part, however, is the description and illustration of the species. The synonymy is brief, being merely sufficient to lead the curious to the major works on the subject, and the descriptions are minimal, being merely sufficient to explain the illustrations. The inclusion of a species does not imply that the author has accepted such species; in many cases he does not and has evidence for their invalidity either from single-cell culture or from ecological evidence of intergrades. The atlas is therefore intended for the ecologist and will probably annoy the dedicated taxonomist. It does permit identification, hopefully by nonspecialists, of specimens found in plankton catches, and such identifications can then be verified by comparing the illustrations with those to be found in the standard works such as Schiller, 1933, 1937.

The author is deeply indebted to Miss Barbara Mathews for a number of the illustrations of the dinoflagellates appearing in this work. This publication is one of the results of a study made under two National Science Foundation grants, GB1494, and GB5625, for which the author is duly indebted.

E.J.F.W.

Miami, Florida
November, 1968

7

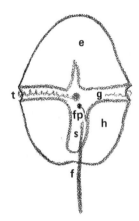

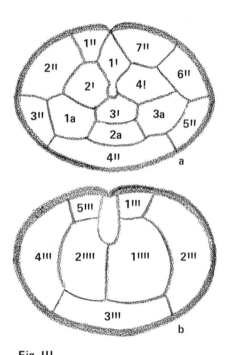

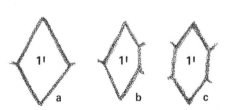

Fig. I.

Terms used for description of naked dino-flagellates (Gymnodiniaceae): e, epicone; g, girdle; h, hypocone; t, transverse flagellum; f, longitudinal flagellum; s, sulcus; fp, flagellar pores.

Fig. III.

Plate formulae of the genus *Peridinium:* a. epitheca, b. hypotheca.

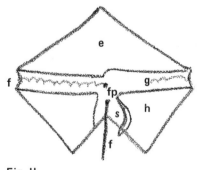

Fig. II.

Terms used for description of armored dinoflagellates (Peridiniaceae): e, epitheca; g, girdle; h, hypotheca; fp, flagellar pores; s, sulcus; f, flagella.

Fig. IV.

Tabulation of Plate 1' of *Peridinium:* (a) ortho, (b) meta, (c) para.

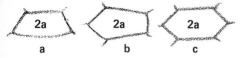

Fig. V.

Tabulation of plate 2a of *Peridinium:* (a) quadra, (b) penta, (c) hexa.

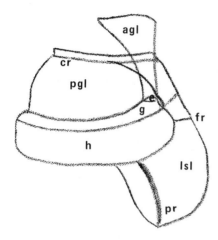

Fig. VI.

Terms used for descriptions of *Histioneis.* The parts can be homologized with other genera of the dinophysidae: agl, anterior girdle list; cr, cross-rib; pgl, posterior girdle list; e, epitheca; g, girdle; fr, fission rib; h, hypotheca; lsl, left sulcal list; pr, posterior rib.

KEY TO THE GENERA

A. Vegetative cells flagellate 1

B. Vegetative cells not flagellate,
   gymnodinioid spores 37

1. Theca absent 2
   Theca present 14
2. Both flagella polar 3
   One flagellum transverse 4
3. No process . . . . *Oxyrrhis*
   Process forming a long tentacle,
   cell kidney-shaped . . . . . . *Noctiluca* ·
   Process or tentacle present, cell pyriform
   or elongate . . . . *Pronoctiluca*
4. Ocellus absent 5
   Ocellus present 10
5. Girdle rudimentary . . . . *Protodinium*
   Girdle strongly anterior *Amphidinium*
   Girdle median or angular 7
   Girdle posterior 6
6. Sulcus confined to small hypocone . . .
   Massartia (Katodinium)
   Sulcus extending to large epicone . . .
   Torodinium
7. Girdle median, displacement slight or
   absent 8
   Girdle median, displacement large . 9
8. Colonial form . . . . *Polykrikos*
   Not colonial . . . . *Gymnodinium*
9. Sulcus spiral . . . . *Cochlodinium*
   Sulcus not spiral . . . . . *Gyrodinium*
10. Girdle displaced, sulcus straight . . . . .
    Protopsis
    Girdle spiral, sulcus twisted 11
11. Nematocysts present . . *Nematodinium*
    Nematocysts absent 12
12. No posteroventral tentacle . . . .
    Warnowia (Pouchetia)
    Tentacle present 13
13. Epicone and hypocone equal . . . . . .
    Protoerythropsis
    Epicone smaller than hypocone . . . . .
    Erythropsis
14. Theca consisting of two plates united
    by a ring 15
    Theca consisting of a number of
    plates 26

15. Both flagella apical 16
    One flagellum transverse 18
16. Cell round to oval, no process . . . 17
    Cell heart-shaped to comma-shaped,
    process present . . . . . *Prorocentrum*
17. Both plates depressed in the middle . .
    Porella
    Plates not depressed . . . . . *Exuviaella*
18. Cells resembling *Amphidinium* but
    thecate . . . . *Thecadinium*
    Cells not resembling *Amphidinium* . . 19
19. Epitheca anterior to girdle lists . . . . .
    Phalacroma
    Anterior girdle list extending forward
    of epitheca 20
20. Posterior girdle list not extending
    beyond epitheca 21
    Posterior girdle list extending beyond
    epitheca 23
21. Body with distinct neck, midbody and
    hindbody 22
    Body with no distinct neck 25
22. Hindbody elongate . . . *Amphisolenia*
    Hindbody consisting of two rearward
    extensions . . . . *Triposolenia*
23. Posterior girdle list with transverse rib
    below margin . . . . *Histioneis*
    No such transverse rib 24
24. Posterior girdle list with less than six
    radial ribs . . . . *Parahistioneis*
    Posterior girdle list with more than six
    radial ribs . . . . *Ornithocercus*
25. Body C-shaped . . . . *Citharistes*
    Body not C-shaped . . . . *Dinophysis*
26. Theca consisting of a large number
    (eighteen or more) plates 27
    Theca consisting of a few plates . . 28
27. Plate 1' (on epitheca above sulcus)
    four-, five-, or six-sided . . . .
    Peridinium (including
    Glenodinium and *Diplopsalis*)
    Plate 1' linear, girdle strongly displaced
    . . . . . *Goniaulax* (including *Spiraulax*)
28. Plates not evident on account of
    markings 29
    Plates more or less evident 30

10

29. Sulcus extending on epitheca . . .
     Melanodinium
    Sulcus not extending on epitheca . . . .
     Protoceratium
30. Girdle not evident 32
    Girdle evident 31
31. Apical horn usually present, if not,
    epitheca much larger than hypotheca . .
     Ceratium
    Epitheca and hypotheca equal or
    subequal 33
    Epitheca smaller than hypotheca . . 36
32. Cells spindle- or pear-shaped . . . . .
     Podolampas
    Cells ovate . . . . *Blepharocysta*
33. Processes on epitheca and hypotheca . .
     Cladopyxis

No processes on epitheca or
hypotheca 34
34. Apical and antapical horns present . . .
     Centrodinium
    No apical or antapical horns 35
35. Cells spherical or polygonal. . . . .
     Goniodoma
    Theca flat-biconical, cells rounded . . . .
     Pyrophacus
36. Epitheca low, equal in width to
    hypotheca . . . . *Ceratocorys*
    Epitheca much smaller than
    hypotheca . . . . *Oxytoxum*
37. Vegetative cells large, spores
    gymnodinioid . . . . *Pyrocystis*
    Vegetative cells small, endophytic,
    spores gymnodinioid . . *Zooxanthellae*

Genus AMPHIDINIUM Claparède and Lachmann

Body usually compressed dorsoventrally and sometimes laterally; girdle far anterior with little or no displacement; sulcus extending from girdle to hypocone or invading epicone, usually not twisted; epicone small, usually asymmetrical; theca absent but cell may be smooth or striate.

Fig. 3

Amphidinium amphidinioides (Geitler) Schiller, 1933

Schiller, 1933, p. 278, fig. 265a-d; *Gymnodinium gymnodinioides* Geitler, 1924, p. 110.

Body elongate-elliptical; epicone rounded-conical, symmetrical; hypocone with rounded base and almost parallel sides; girdle circular, indented, very slightly left-handed; sulcus not reaching apex or base. Length 25 μ.

Lower Austria. Cat Cay, Straits of Florida.

Fig. 1

Amphidinium acutissimum Schiller, 1933

Schiller, 1933, p. 277, fig. 263; Wood, 1963a, p. 22, fig. 68.

Epicone small, dome–shaped; hypocone with convex margins, tapering to a sharp point; girdle flat, upper margin ill-defined. Length 20 μ.

Adriatic Sea; Coral and North Tasman seas. Straits of Florida; Caribbean Sea.

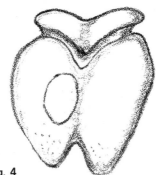

Fig. 4

Amphidinium bipes Herdman, 1924

Herdman, 1924, p. 78, fig. 19; Schiller, 1933, p. 280, fig. 267.

Body indentate slightly at apex, deeply at base; epicone triangular with slightly concave apex, left side slightly higher; hypocone with convex sides and strongly concave base; girdle deeply indented; sulcus not reaching base; colorless. Length 30 μ.

Isle of Man. West Channel, south of Key West.

Fig. 2

Amphidinium acutum Lohmann, 1920

Lohmann, 1920, p. 140, fig. 43; Schiller, 1933, p. 278, fig. 264.

Body thin; epicone small, triangular; hypocone much larger, wedge-shaped, widest at girdle; girdle wide and deep. Length 25 μ. Similar to *Oxytoxum*.

Mediterranean Sea; Atlantic Ocean. Straits of Florida; Caribbean Sea.

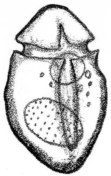

Fig. 7

Amphidinium glaucum Conrad, 1926

Conrad, 1926, p. 75, pl. 1, figs. 3-5; Wood, 1963b, p. 9, fig. 23.

Body ovate to almost spherical; epicone very small, flattened, asymmetrical; hypocone slightly asymmetrical, left shoulder higher than right; antapex broadly rounded; girdle circular; sulcus running from girdle, narrowing on hypocone. Length 35 μ.

Belgium (in brackish waters); Indonesian waters. Caribbean Sea.

Fig. 5

Amphidinium crassum Lohmann, 1908

Lohmann, 1908, p. 252, pl. 17, fig. 16; Schiller, 1933, p. 283, fig. 272a-c.

Body broadly oval; epicone small, conical, sides rounded; hypocone broader, longer than broad, base rounded; girdle wide and deep, even; sulcus extending to apex and nearly to base. Length 30 μ.

English Channel; Adriatic Sea. Straits of Florida.

Fig. 6

Amphidinium flagellans Schiller, 1928

Schiller, 1928, p. 136, fig. 13a-b; Schiller, 1933, p. 291, fig. 283a-b; Wood, 1963a, p. 23, fig. 72.

Body bluntly fusiform, not flattened dorsoventrally; epicone subconical, pointed; hypocone rounded, tapering to antapex; girdle deep and broad; sulcus narrow on epicone, wide and tapering on hypocone, left margin slightly higher. Length 20-25 μ.

Adriatic Sea; Coral Sea. Straits of Florida.

Fig. 8

Amphidinium globosum Schröder, 1911

Schröder, 1911, pp. 616, 651, fig. 16; Wood, 1963b, p. 9, fig. 24.

Body rotund, oval; epicone low, symmetrical; apex flat to convex, smaller than hypocone; hypocone broad, almost spherical; girdle deep; sulcus broad, tapering toward antapex. Length 40-50 μ.

Indonesian waters. Bahama Banks Midchannel; Cat Cay, Straits of Florida; Benguela Current.

Fig. 9

Amphidinium kesslitzi Schiller, 1928

Schiller, 1928, p. 135, fig. 11, pl. 5 (fig. 12); Schiller, p. 297, fig. 291a-b; Wood, 1954, p. 218, fig. 78.

Epicone capitate, almost spherical; hypocone oval; girdle deep; sulcus more than half as long as hypocone. Length 7-10 μ.

Adriatic Sea; southwest Pacific Ocean. Caribbean Sea.

Fig. 11

Amphidinium lacustriforme Schiller, 1928

Schiller, 1928, p. 132, fig. 6; Schiller, 1933, p. 300, fig. 295.

Epicone very small, flat; hypocone subcordate with rounded base, flattened dorsoventrally; girdle indented; sulcus not on epicone, V-shaped from girdle; reaching the middle of hypocone. Length 10 μ.

Estuarine in Adriatic Sea. Straits of Florida.

Fig. 10

Amphidinium klebsi Kofoid and Swezy, 1921

Kofoid and Swezy, 1921; Wood, 1954, p. 218, fig. 79. *A. carteri* Wood (synonym).

Cells oval, rounded posteriorly; girdle extending down hypocone for about one-half its length; sulcus extending from girdle obliquely to right, ending on right side; epicone tongue-shaped, deflected to left; flagellar pores approximate near junction of girdle and sulcus. Length 30-40 μ.

Isle of Man; Cullercoats; Gulf of Naples; Adriatic Sea, Port Hacking (Australia). Straits of Florida; Pigeon Key; Biscayne Bay, common; Key Largo; culture at IMS; recorded by Hulburt (1962): Benguela Current; Brazil (north coast); Caribbean Sea.

Fig. 12

Amphidinium lanceolatum Schröder, 1911

Schröder, 1911, p. 650, fig. 15; Schiller, 1933, p. 301, fig. 296.

Body elongate, cylindrical with acute antapex and rounded apical region; epicone minute; sulcus about one-quarter body length. Length 30-40 μ.

Adriatic Sea. Amazon region.

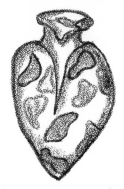

Fig. 13

Amphidinium operculatum Claparède and Lachmann, 1858-1861

Claparède and Lachmann, 1858-1861, p. 410, pl. 20 (figs. 9-10); Schiller, 1933, p. 304, fig. 304a-g.

Body elliptical; epicone small, cordate; hypocone oval, nucleus posterior; girdle ovate, continuous with sulcus and reaching base; chromatophores radiate. Length 35-50 μ.

Atlantic Ocean; Mediterranean Sea; saline to fresh water. Straits of Florida.

Fig. 14

Amphidinium schroederi Schiller, 1928

Schiller, 1928, p. 134, fig. 10; Schiller, 1933, p. 313, fig. 314a-b.

Epicone very small, asymmetrical with a ventral peak, apex rounded; hypocone cordate, with bluntly pointed base; girdle deep and wide, continuing backward into narrow sulcus which reaches about half length of hypocone. Length about 20 μ.

Adriatic Sea. Straits of Florida.

Fig. 13.1

Amphidinium phaeocysticola Lebour, 1925

Lebour, 1925, p. 31, pl. 3 (fig. 3a-c); Schiller, 1933, p. 310, fig. 310a-c.

Epicone conical, low; hypocone slightly constricted just below girdle, then rounded, base with or without irregular protuberance; girdle deep and wide, slightly left-handed; sulcus reaching from apex nearly to antapex, widest in the middle of the hypocone; surface striped. Length 42 μ.

Plymouth Sound. Straits of Florida.

Fig. 15

Amphidinium sphenoides Wulff, 1916

Wulff, 1916, p. 105, pl. 1, fig. 9a-b; Schiller, 1933, p. 315, fig. 318a-b; Wood, 1963*a*, p. 23, fig. 73.

Body spindle-shaped; epicone triangular, smaller than triangular hypocone; apex and antapex acute; girdle deep and narrow; sulcus small. Length 40 μ.

Barents Sea; Solomon Islands. Straits of Florida.

Fig. 16

Fig. 15.1

Amphidinium testudo Herdman, 1924

Herdman, 1924, p. 76, figs. 2-5; Lebour, 1925, p. 29, fig. 8e.

Body ovate; epicone very small, flat or slightly crenate; hypocone oval, base round; girdle deep, cordate; with small sulcus. Length 20-30 μ.

In sand at Port Erin, Isle of Man; Woods Hole, Mass. Straits of Florida.

Amphidinium turbo Kofoid and Swezy, 1921

Kofoid and Swezy, 1921, p. 155, pl. 9 (fig. 98); Wood, 1963a, p. 23, fig. 74.

Epicone small, elliptical; hypocone cordate; girdle anterior, not displaced, broad. Length 20-30 μ.

California coast; Coral Sea, Straits of Florida; Benguela Current; Brazil (north coast); Caribbean Sea.

Genus AMPHIDOMA Stein

Body more or less biconical; girdle circular, slightly displaced, central or somewhat posterior; apical horn and antapical spine may be present; plate formula 6', Oa, 6'', 6''', 1p, 1''''.

Genus AMPHILOTHUS (Schütt) Kofoid

Frustule biconical to ovate with both ends somewhat acute; girdle narrow to moderate, depressed; sulcus absent; with an outer membrane over the skeleton.

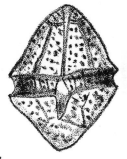

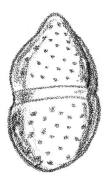

Fig. 17

Amphidoma steini Schiller, 1929

Schiller, 1929, p. 399, fig. 10a-b; Schiller, 1937, p. 315, fig. 331a-b.

Body broadly biconical with convex sides; apex bluntly conical; antapex acute, without spine; girdle broad, depressed, porulate; sulcus small, not reaching base; plate formula 6', Oa, 6'', 6''', 1p, 1''''. Length 40-50 μ.

Mediterranean Sea. Caribbean Sea.

Fig. 18

Amphilothus quincuncialis Kofoid, 1907

Kofoid, 1907b, p. 206, pl. 1 (fig. 10); Schiller, 1937, p. 8. fig. 5.

Body elliptical; girdle median, depressed, no lists; sulcus straight, reaching from end to end; epitheca subconical; hypotheca rounded; skeleton porulate. Length 35 μ.

Panama; Straits of Florida.

17

Genus AMPHISOLENIA Stein

Epitheca small, flat or rounded; girdle much anterior with small lists; sulcal lists inconspicuous; hypotheca very elongate, consisting of a thin neck, swollen midbody, and tapering antapical extension, all colinear but antapex may be curved, sigmoid, or branched, with two or more small spinelets.

Fig. 19

Amphisolenia bidentata Schröder, 1900

Schröder, 1900; Wood, 1954, p. 205, fig. 55.

Slightly or moderately sigmoid; head two to three times wider than long; epitheca gently convex; midbody fusiform, merging gradually into anterior and antapical portions; antapical twisted ventrally and bent to the right with spinule at elbow; antapex widened truncate with two spinules on left valve, none on right. Length 700-900 μ.

Worldwide in tropical and warm, temperate seas; oceanic. Not uncommon in Straits of Florida; Benguela Current; Caribbean Sea.

Fig. 20

Amphisolenia bifurcata Murray and Whitting, 1899

Murray and Whitting, 1899, p. 331, figs. 7-9, pl. 31 (fig. 1a-e); Wood, 1963a, p. 9, fig. 21.

Hypotheca almost straight; fusiform to bifurcate antapical region, two legs being subequal or of slightly different lengths, somewhat swollen anteriorly, distal parts spinulate. Length 85 μ.

Pacific Ocean; Indian Ocean; Tropical Atlantic Ocean and Caribbean Sea; Straits of Florida.

Fig. 21

Amphisolenia bispinosa Kofoid, 1907

Kofoid, 1907a, pp. 197, 201, pl. 4 (fig. 85); Schiller, 1933, p. 175, fig. 163.

Body not much swollen; neck short and straight; midbody even width, tapering slightly into caudal portion, which is slightly bent at base and terminated by two spinules. Length 600-650 μ.

Tropical Pacific and Atlantic oceans. Straits of Florida.

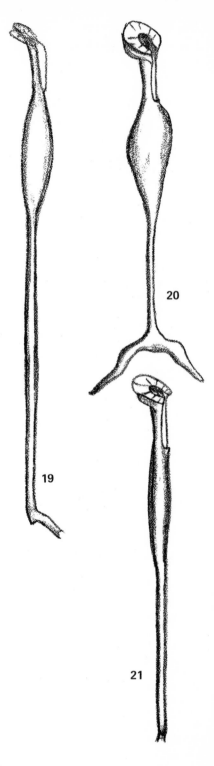

20

19

21

Fig. 22

Amphisolenia clavipes Kofoid, 1907

Kofoid, 1907*b*, p. 14, fig. 90; Wood, 1963*a*, p. 9, fig. 23.

Body fusiform, anterior and antapical portions short; epitheca convex, low; hypotheca bent more or less sharply near antapex, widened at end with two spinules but no spinule at elbow. Length 250 μ

Eastern tropical Pacific Ocean, off Fiji and south of New Caledonia. Straits of Florida; Brazil (north coast).

Fig. 23

Amphisolenia curvata Kofoid, 1907

Kofoid, 1907*b*, p. 197, pl. 14, fig. 87; Kofoid and Skogsberg, 1928, p. 398, fig. 49 (11), pl. 9 (figs. 5, 9-10).

Midbody swollen, antapical region moderately wide, evenly curved ventrally toward antapex, with two small spines. Length 460 μ.

Tropical Pacific and Atlantic oceans.

Fig. 24

Amphisolenia extensa Kofoid, 1907

Kofoid, 1907*a*, p. 198, pl. 13 (fig. 78); Kofoid and Skogsberg, 1928, p. 383, fig. 49 (8), pl. 6 (figs. 3, 5).

Body very elongate; neck and midbody small and thin; hindbody very long, slightly bent toward antapex. Length 1,200-1,500 μ. Probably identical with *A. spinosa* and *A. elongata* from which it differs chiefly in size, other differential characters being variable in this genus.

Pacific and Atlantic oceans; Mediterranean Sea. Straits of Florida.

Fig. 25

Amphisolenia globifera Stein, 1883

Stein, 1883, p. 24, pl. 21 (figs. 9-10); Wood, 1963*a*, p. 10, fig. 24.

Body straight or slightly sigmoid; hypotheca swollen anteriorly; antapex characteristically globose, bidentate. Length 150-200 μ.

Atlantic Ocean and Indian Ocean off Australia; eastern Pacific Ocean and Coral Sea. Straits of Florida, fairly common; Benguela Current; Brazil (north coast); Caribbean Sea.

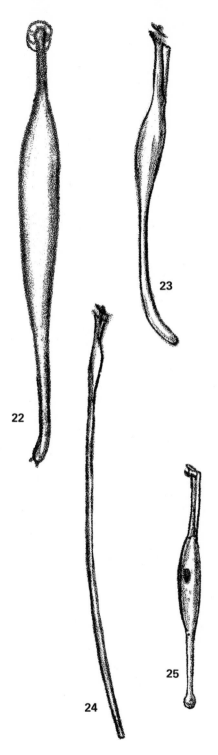

23

22

24

25

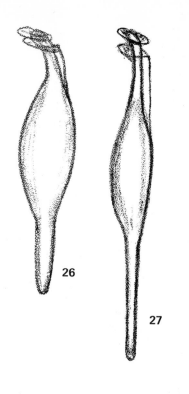

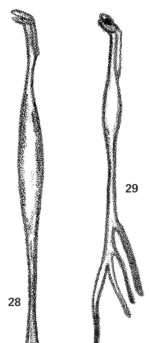

26

27

28

29

Fig. 26

Amphisolenia inflata Murray and Whitting, 1899

Murray and Whitting, 1899, p. 332, pl. 31 (fig. 2a-b); Schiller, 1933, p. 167, fig. 152.

Body straight; head broader than long; epitheca concave; midbody very swollen, ovate; antapex straight with acute end with two spinules. Length 120-130 μ.

Worldwide in warm seas; Mediterranean and adjacent seas. Straits of Florida.

Fig. 27

Amphisolenia laticincta Kofoid, 1907

Kofoid, 1907*b*, p. 198, pl. 13 (fig. 80); Wood, 1963*b*, p. 5, fig. 9.

Body straight, swollen in the middle, spindle-shaped, extended antapically; girdle unusually wide, anterior and posterior girdle lists therefore widely separated. Length 130 μ.

Coral Sea. Straits of Florida; Caribbean Sea.

Fig. 28

Amphisolenia palaeotheroides Kofoid, 1907

Kofoid, 1907*b*, p. 199, pl. 14, fig. 84; Wood, 1963*a*, p. 10, fig. 26.

Body almost straight; hypotheca fusiform, tapering gently from swollen middle in both directions; antapical portion slightly broadened, tridentate. Length 500 μ.

Peruvian Current, Easter Islands; South Equatorial drift; Coral Sea. Santaren Channel, Straits of Florida; Caribbean Sea.

Fig. 29

Amphisolenia quadricauda Kofoid and Michener, 1911

Kofoid and Michener, 1911, p. 293; Kofoid and Skogsberg, 1928, p. 445, pl. 13 (figs. 7, 9, 14).

Body straight, midbody swollen, tapering into a four-fingered extension which is slightly sigmoid. Length 700-1,000 μ.

Tropical Pacific Ocean; western tropical Atlantic Ocean. Caribbean Sea.

Fig. 30

Amphisolenia quadrispina Kofoid, 1907

Kofoid, 1907*b*, pp. 200-201, pl. 14 (fig. 86); Schiller, 1933, p. 174, fig. 162a-b.

Body straight and narrow; neck and caudal portion elongate; base slightly expanded, with four spinules. Length 600-700 μ.

Tropical and subtropical Pacific and Atlantic oceans. Straits of Florida.

Fig. 31

Amphisolenia schauinslandi Lemmermann, 1899

Lemmermann, 1899, pp. 317, 350, 373, fig. 19; Wood, 1963*a*, p. 10, fig. 28.

Body straight; head capitate; epitheca flattened; hypotheca fusiform, posterior part short, straight; antapex with four spinules. Length 200-400 μ.

Tropical and subtropical Indian Ocean; Gulf of Aden; tropical Pacific Ocean; Coral Sea. Straits of Florida; Caribbean Sea.

Fig. 32

Amphisolenia spinulosa Kofoid, 1907

Kofoid, 1907*b*, p. 315, pl. 32 (figs. 53-55); Kofoid and Skogsberg, 1928, pp. 353, 360, 365, 379.

Body very long and thin; neck and midbody relatively short; hindbody long and thin, slightly curved, with three small spines. Length 740-800 μ. Possibly identical with *A. extensa* and *A. elongata*.

American coast of Pacific Ocean. Straits of Florida.

Fig. 33

Amphisolenia thrinax Schütt, 1893

Schütt, 1893, pp. 271, 299, 301, fig. 81; Wood, 1954, p. 206, pl. 57a-b.

Body slightly sigmoid; midbody fusiform; antapex with three branches, posterior part with small "heel" and two spines on each branch. Length 100-200 μ.

Brazil (north coast).

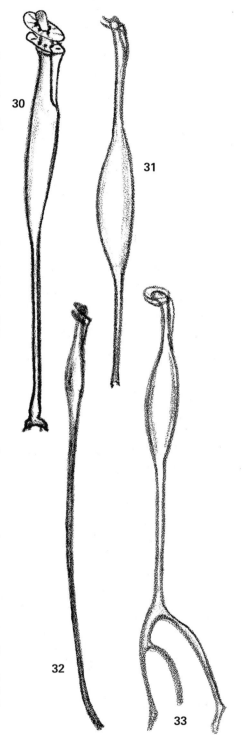

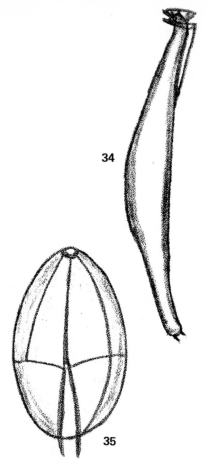

Fig. 34

Amphisolenia sp.

Midbody large, tapering into neck and hindbody, ventrally concave, dorsally convex with inflated midbody; antapex slightly swollen, with two spines. Length 200 μ. Possibly related to *A. globifera* Stein.

Caribbean Sea, on 75th parallel at 60-80m.

Genus BLEPHAROCYSTA Ehrenberg

Theca spherical to oval; apical pore surrounded by a list but no apical horn; margins of equatorial and postequatorial plates form a ring which replaces the girdle; sulcus even, with two wings which extend beyond the base; plate formula 1', 5", 5"', 3"".

Fig. 35

Blepharocysta splendormaris (Ehrenberg) Ehrenberg, 1859

Blepharocysta splendor maris Ehrenberg, 1873; Wood, 1963a, p. 51, fig. 188; *Peridinium splendor maris* Ehrenberg, 1859, p. 791.

Body ovate with apical pore, marked plate margins, two posterior wings extending from girdle region. Length 50 μ.

North Sea; Coral Sea; Mediterranean Sea; off d'Entrecasteaux. Frequent in the Straits of Florida, Bahama Banks, and Pigeon Key; Benguela Current; Brazil (north coast); Caribbean Sea.

Genus CENTRODINIUM Kofoid

Body subrotund with strong twisted apical horn and apical pore; antapical horn single, twisted, ribbed; girdle wide.

Fig. 36

Centrodinium intermedium Pavillard, 1930

Pavillard, 1930, p. 11, fig. 13; Schiller, 1937, p. 436, fig. 478a-c.

Body ovate; girdle submedian; apical horn rather short, blunt; antapical horn angled, twisted, blunt, longer than apical. Length 100 μ

Mediterranean Sea. Tropical Atlantic Ocean; Caribbean Sea; Brazil (north coast).

Genus CERATIUM Schrank

Theca usually flattened dorsoventrally, drawn out into hollow horns; girdle left-handed; sulcus very wide, almost circular; epitheca rounded with apical and ventral pores as in *Heterodinium (Archaeceratium),* or forming a more or less attenuated apical horn which may be straight or bent; hypotheca drawn out into one or two equal or unequal antapical horns, which may be open or closed or may extend posteriorly or curve forward toward the apex.

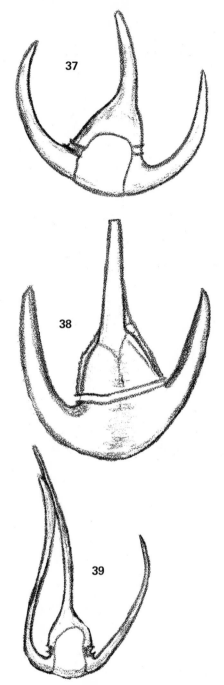

37

38

39

Fig. 37

Ceratium arietinum Cleve, 1900

Cleve, 1900, p. 13, pl. y (fig. 3); Wood, 1954, p. 294, fig. 221a-e; Hulburt, 1963.

Medium-sized species; apical horn somewhat bent to left at base, then straight or again slightly bent to the left toward apex; left antapical horn evenly curved, usually more or less converging, rarely parallel; right antapical very strong and evenly curved right to the tip, somewhat twisted. Length 50-75 μ.

Tasman Sea (East Australian current); Indian Ocean off Australia; interoceanic warm-water form. Straits of Florida; West Channel, Gulf Stream (Hulburt, 1963); Benguela Current; Brazil (north coast); Caribbean Sea.

Fig. 38

Ceratium axiale Kofoid, 1907

Kofoid, 1907a, p. 170, pl. 4 (fig. 26); Wood, 1954, p. 294, fig. 219.

Apical horn bent to the right, shoulders narrowly rounded; antapical horns turning sharply forward, right almost parallel with apical horn, left shorter than right, more distant from body. Length 50-60 μ.

Tropical Pacific and Atlantic and probably Indian oceans. Straits of Florida.

Fig. 39

Ceratium azoricum Cleve, 1900

Cleve, 1900, p. 13, pl. 7 (figs. 6, 7); Schiller, 1937, p. 406, fig. 447; Wood, 1954, p. 295, fig. 222a-b.

Body flat, curved laterally; large epitheca high, slightly angular, tapering into apical horn; hypotheca round, continuous with both antapicals which are thick, tapering, closed, ending parallel with apical horn; wings present on apical horn. Length 50-60 μ.

Rare in tropical and subtropical waters; interoceanic. Benguela Current (not infrequent); Straits of Florida; Brazil (north coast).

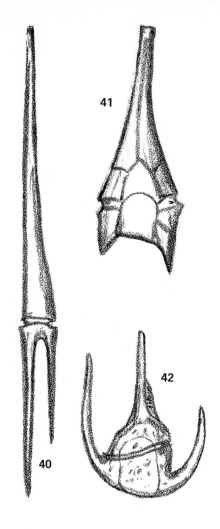

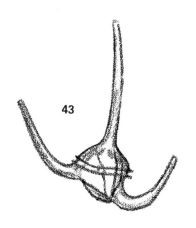

Fig. 40

Ceratium belone Cleve, 1900

Cleve, 1900, p. 3, pl. 7 (fig. 13); Schiller, 1937, p. 360, fig. 407a; Wood, 1954, p. 275.

A large species with straight apical and antapical horns; apical tapering gradually from girdle to apex; antapicals parallel, left much stronger than right; sulcus narrow, parallel-sided; horns thickened markedly. Length 150-200 μ.

Rare tropical species, interoceanic. Benguela Current; Northwest Providence Channel, Straits of Florida; Brazil (north coast); Caribbean Sea.

Fig. 41

Ceratium brachyceros Daday, 1907

Daday, 1907, p. 245, fig. A; Schiller, 1937, p. 362, fig. 398a-b.

Epitheca tapering more or less evenly into a somewhat wide apical horn; hypotheca low, with two horns of almost equal length; theca thick, reticulate. Length 100-200 μ.

Tropical fresh-water species in Africa and Asia. Florida Everglades.

Fig. 42

Ceratium breve (Ostenfeld and Schmidt) Schröder, 1906.

Schröder, 1906, p. 358, *C. tripos* var. *brevis* Ostenfeld and Schmidt, 1901, p. 164, fig. 13.

Robust species; epitheca more than half as long as broad, left contour steep, right strongly and broadly convex; hypotheca as long as or longer than epitheca, base contour even or swollen in middle, horns strong, antapicals evenly curved forward; theca porulate, ridged. Length 100-200 μ.

Brazil (north coast); Caribbean Sea.

Fig. 43

Ceratium buceros (Zacharias) Schiller, 1937

Schiller, 1937, p. 415, fig. 456; Wood, 1954, p. 301, fig. 231a-i; Zacharias, 1906, p. 551.

Body small, longer than broad, base markedly convex, sometimes sunken; all horns thin, may be spinulate or clavate. This species has many forms which often occur together. Length 50-100 μ.

Estuarine-neritic, sometimes oceanic, cosmopolitan species. West Channel, Straits of Florida; Benguela Current; Brazil (north coast);Caribbean Sea.

Fig. 44

Ceratium candelabrum (Ehrenberg) Stein, 1883

Stein, 1883, pl. 15 (figs. 14-16); Schiller, 1937, p. 364, figs. 401-403; Wood, 1954, p. 273, fig. 187a-b; *Peridinium candelabrum* Ehrenberg, 1859, p. 792.

Body broader than high; epitheca obliquely conical, tapering into a long apical horn which is straight or slightly bent; hypotheca very shallow, triangular; antapicals varying, usually thick and straight or slightly curved, widely separated laterally. Length 100-200 μ.

Common in warm, temperate seas; oceanic. Straits of Florida; Benguela Current; Brazil (north coast); Caribbean Sea.

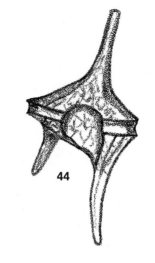

44

Fig. 45

Ceratium carolinianum (Bailey) Jörgensen, 1911

Jörgensen, 1911, p. 14, figs. 17-18; Schiller, 1937, p. 364, fig. 400.

Epitheca low, wide; apical horn thick, strongly deflected to the right; hypotheca broader than epitheca, shallow; right antapical horn short and thick, directed sideways; left antapical longer and directed posteriorly. Length 80 μ.

Fresh water lakes of Scotland, Norway, and North America. Florida Everglades.

Fig. 46

Ceratium carriense Gourret, 1883

Gourret, 1883, pl. 4 (fig. 57); Schiller, 1937, p. 425, figs. 464-466; Wood, 1954, p. 308, fig. 236a-b.

Probably synonymous with *C. massiliense*. Contains those forms with very long horns; body small to moderate; epitheca rounded; hypotheca with indented base. Body length 60-70 μ.

Endemic in tropical oceanic waters. Cat Cay and West Channel, Straits of Florida; Benguela Current; Caribbean Sea.

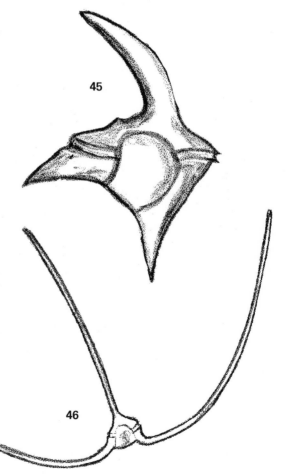

45

46

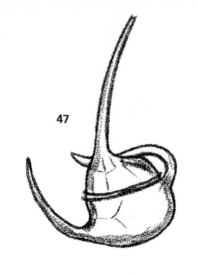

Fig. 47

Ceratium concilians Jörgensen, 1920

Jörgensen, 1920, p. 72, fig. 69; Schiller, 1937, p. 396, fig. 435a-b; Wood, 1954, p. 290, fig. 213.

Like *C. gibberum* but smaller; body not humped and basal contour much less swollen to the left; theca smooth and without the strong ribs characteristic of *C. gibberum;* right antapical continuous with base, bent toward dorsal side of body, distal end often bent again in direction of apical horn or at right angles thereto. Length 200 μ. Transitions to *C. gibberum* occur.

Tropical interoceanic form extending into subtropical waters. Straits of Florida; Caribbean Sea.

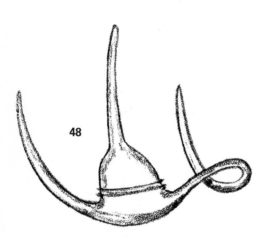

Fig. 48

Ceratium contortum (Gourret) Cleve, 1900

Cleve, 1900, p. 15, pl. 7 (fig. 10); Wood, 1954, p. 289, fig. 212a-c.

Epitheca oblique on right, right contour strongly convex; apical horn clearly bent to the left and twisted, almost S-shaped; base contour convex, more or less swollen; antapicals more or less unequal, the right usually longer than the left, the latter like that of *C. karsteni*, the former twisted dorsally or ventrally and then forward. Length 200-500 μ.

Warm-water species in all oceans. Straits of Florida.

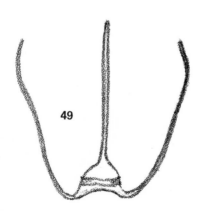

Fig. 49

Ceratium contrarium (Gourret) Pavillard, 1905

Pavillard, 1905, p. 53, pl. 2 (fig. 1); Jörgensen, 1920, p. 93, fig. 84; *C. trichoceros* var. *contrarium* (Gourret) Schiller, 1937, p. 431, fig. 471; *C. tripos* var. *contrarium* Gourret, 1883, pl. 3 (fig. 51).

Body small; apical horn long and straight; antapicals arising below base, directed toward transverse axis and then forward, curving outward about halfway to tips and then often forward again. Length 200-400 μ.

In all warm oceans and seas. Straits of Florida; Caribbean Sea.

Fig. 50

Ceratium declinatum Karsten, 1907

Karsten, 1907, pl. 48, fig. 2a-b; Wood, 1954, p. 293, fig. 218a-c.

A small, delicate species; body flattened, longer than broad, all three horns within body plane; apical horn usually straight, but not quite at right angles to girdle; hypotheca shorter than high epitheca, base round, continuous with antapicals; left antapicals shorter or longer than body, stronger than right which is longer, end closed, almost parallel to apical horn but right may bend at tip. Length 40-60 μ.

Tropical species, interoceanic. Cat Cay, Santaren Channel, Straits of Florida; Brazil (north coast); Caribbean Sea.

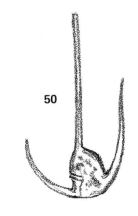

50

Fig. 51

Ceratium deflexum (Kofoid) Jörgensen, 1911

Jörgensen, 1911, p. 64, figs. 138-139; Wood, 1954, p. 310, fig. 237; *C. macroceros deflexum* Kofoid, 1907a, p. 304.

Apical horn straight; antapicals directed backward and then strongly ventrally and forward; regarded by Kofoid (1907a) as a form of *C. macroceros.* Length 50-70 μ.

Rare warm-water species in the Indian and Pacific oceans. Straits of Florida.

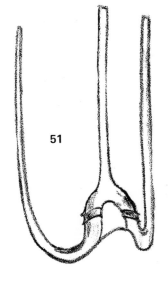

51

Fig. 52

Ceratium digitatum Schütt, 1895

Schütt, 1895, p. 12, fig. 42; Wood, 1963a, p. 39, fig. 144.

Epitheca swollen, strongly bent dorsally, in ventral view somewhat flat, sharply bent, tapering obtusely to a blunt point; antapical horns very unlike, the left strongly sigmoid, bent forward and then turned backward, right much shorter, straight, tapering to a sharp point. Length 100 μ.

Rare in warm waters; Pacific and Atlantic oceans. Caribbean Sea.

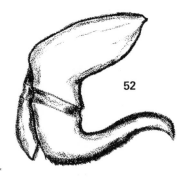

52

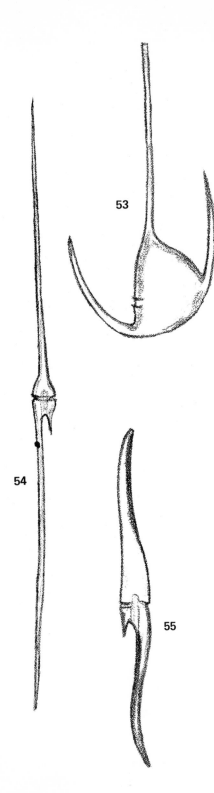

Fig. 53

Ceratium euarcuatum Jörgensen, 1920

Jörgensen, 1920, p. 56, fig. 54; Schiller, 1937, p. 402, fig. 443; Wood, 1954, p. 294, fig. 220a-b.

Small species; body much longer than broad; epitheca rounded; girdle incomplete; left antapical arising from girdle region or anterior to it, parallel to or converging on apical horn; hypotheca with round base continuous with fine, tapered antapical horns, right horn with base at right angles to that of left antapical and apical horns. Length 100-150 μ.

Tropical oceans. Rare in Straits of Florida.

Fig. 54

Ceratium extensum (Gourret) Cleve, 1901

Cleve, 1901, p. 215; Schiller, 1937, p. 380, fig. 419a-b; Wood, 1954, p. 283, fig. 203a-b.

A very long species similar in shape to *C. fusus;* epitheca long and narrow, continuous with a long, straight, narrow apical horn; left antapical usually long, diverted slightly dorsally but straight; right antapical absent or needle-like, small; epitheca usually shorter than hypotheca. Length 500-1,200 μ.

Tropical oceanic form, usually sparse; interoceanic. Sargasso Sea (Hulburt *et al.,* 1960); West Channel, Straits of Florida; Benguela Current; Brazil (north coast); Caribbean Sea.

Fig. 55

Ceratium falcatiforme Jörgensen, 1920

Jörgensen, 1920, p.40, fig. 29; Schiller, 1937, p. 378, fig. 417b; Wood, 1954, p. 282, fig. 201a-b.

Similar to *C. longirostrum* and *C. falcatum,* but apical horn thicker and more curved, with more gradual transition from epitheca to apical horn; antapical horn thicker. Length 200 μ.

Interoceanic tropical species, extending into subtropics. Straits of Florida; Caribbean Sea.

Fig. 56

Ceratium falcatum (Kofoid) Jörgensen, 1920

Jörgensen, 1920; *C. pennatum* f. *falcata* Kofoid, 1907*b*, p. 172, pl. 2 (fig. 14).

Body linear; apical and left antapical horns bent about two-thirds length; right antapical small, acicular. Length 200 *μ*.

Interoceanic warm-water species; Mediterranean Sea; Pacific Ocean. Brazil (north coast); Benguela Current; Caribbean Sea.

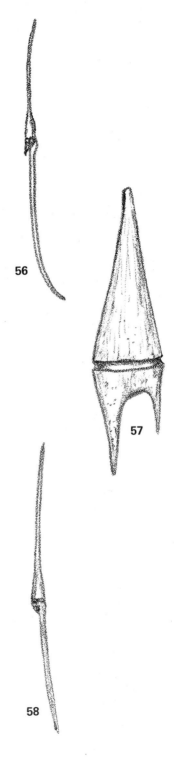

56

57

Fig. 57

Ceratium furca (Ehrenberg) Claparède and Lachmann, 1858-1861

Claparède and Lachmann, 1858-1861, p. 399, pl. 19 (fig. 5); Schiller, 1937, p. 367, figs. 404-405; Wood, 1954, p. 274, fig. 189; *Peridinium furca* Ehrenberg, 1883, p. 270.

Body straight; epitheca tapering gradually into apical horn; hypotheca varying from parallel-sided to tapering from girdle; antapicals strong, unequal, usually straight, parallel to subparallel, may be toothed. Length 70-100 *μ*.

Cosmopolitan, except in Antarctic waters. Gulf Stream (Hulburt, 1963); Gulf of Mexico (Curl, 1959); Santaren Channel, Straits of Florida; Benguela Current; Brazil (north coast); Florida Everglades; Caribbean Sea.

Fig. 58

Ceratium fusus (Ehrenberg) Dujardin, 1841

Dujardin, 1841; Schiller, 1937, p. 378, fig. 418a-b; Wood, 1954, p. 282, fig. 202; *Peridinium fusus* Ehrenberg, 1833, p. 271.

Medium to small species; epitheca long, gradually tapering to a cylindrical or gently tapering apical horn, usually slightly bent dorsally or straight; hypotheca tapering; left antapical long, slightly curved, rarely straight; right antapical rudimentary or absent. Length 200-300 *μ*.

Cosmopolitan except in Antarctic and sub-Antarctic waters. Sargasso Sea (Hulburt, *et al.*, 1960); Gulf Stream (Hulburt, 1963); Gulf of Mexico (Curl, 1959); Benguela Current; Pigeon Key; Santaren Channel, West Channel, Straits of Florida; Brazil (north coast); Caribbean Sea.

58

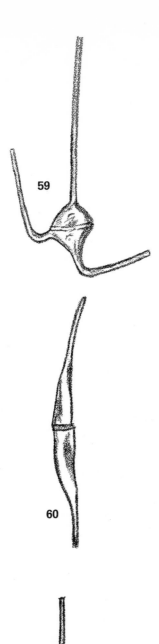

Fig. 59

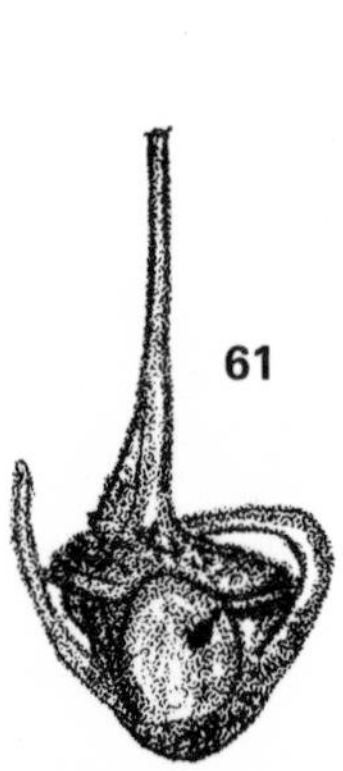

Ceratium gallicum Kofoid, 1907

Kofoid, 1907*a*, p. 302, pl. 24, figs. 10-12; *C. macroceros* sub sp. *gallicum* Jörgensen, 1911.

A delicate species with almost square body; long slender apical horn; deeply indented base; and slender antapicals extending posteriorly, then curved out and forward. Body length 40-50 μ.

Tropical species, interoceanic. Straits of Florida; Brazil (north coast); Caribbean Sea.

Fig. 60

Ceratium geniculatum (Lemmermann) Cleve, 1901

Cleve, 1901; Schiller 1937, p. 375, fig. 414a; Wood, 1963*a*, p. 40, fig. 145a-b.

Medium-sized species; epitheca in ventral view narrowed above girdle, then swollen, and constricted into apical horn, about the same length as the epitheca; hypotheca short; left antapical strong, usually bent twice, directed posteriorly, thick-walled; right antapical posterior, short to rudimentary. Length 200-500 μ.

Tropical species. Straits of Florida, rare; Brazil (north coast).

Fig. 61

Ceratium gibberum Gourret, 1883

Gourret, 1883, p. 36, pl. 2 (fig. 35); Schiller, 1937, p. 397, fig. 436a-b; Wood, 1954, p. 290, fig. 214a-b.

Body thick, rather flattened; epitheca low, angled strongly on left, somewhat humped; hypotheca rounded to gibbous, longer than epitheca; left antapical strong, evenly bent, tip closed, directed anteriorly; right antapical based close to girdle, transverse, then curved rapidly behind dorsal surface of epitheca, tip closed, directed transversely or slightly forward. Length 100-150 μ.

Tropical species, never abundant, oceanic. Gulf of Mexico (Curl, 1959); Benguela Current; Brazil (north coast); Caribbean Sea.

Fig. 62

Ceratium gravidum Gourret, 1883

Gourret, 1883, p. 58, pl. 1 (fig. 15); Schiller, 1937, p. 357, fig. 389; Wood, 1954, p. 272, fig. 186a-c.

Epitheca without horn, ovate, apex broadly rounded, broadening rapidly above girdle; pore in lower part of epitheca; hypotheca narrowing from girdle with two strong, straight or curved antapical horns. Length 300-400 μ.

Tropical oceanic species. Northwest Providence Channel, Straits of Florida; Benguela Current; Caribbean Sea.

Fig. 63

Ceratium hexacanthum Gourret, 1883

Gourret, 1883, p. 36, pl. 3 (fig. 49); Schiller, 1937, p. 421, fig. 426a-c; Wood, 1954, p. 306, fig. 234a-b; *C. reticulatum* (Pouchet) Cleve, 1903, p. 342.

Body concave, very strongly marked with reticulations, bottom toothed; apical horn straight; antapicals curled spirally, right antapical whip-like. Size variable.

Tropical to subtropical. Straits of Florida; Brazil (north coast); Caribbean Sea.

Fig. 64

Ceratium hirundinella (O. F. Müller) Bergh, 1882

Bergh, 1882, p. 215, pl. 13 (fig. 12); Schiller, 1937, p. 359, figs. 393-397; *Bursaria hirundinella* O. F. Müller, 1773, p. 63.

Cell flattened dorsoventrally; epitheca conical, tapering into a long or short apical horn; hypotheca with normally three, more rarely two, antapical horns pointing rearward, rarely one pointing sideways. Length 140-200 μ.

Generally in fresh water but has been found in the Coral Sea and Timor Sea. Florida Everglades.

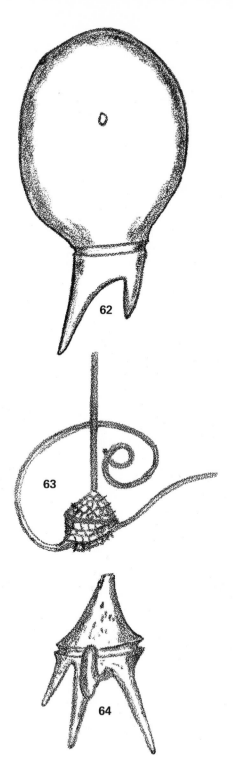

62

63

64

31

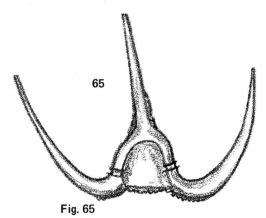

65

forward; right antapical longer, directed somewhat forward at base, parallel to apical or slightly converging. Length 200 μ.

Tropical oceanic species. Northwest Providence Channel, Straits of Florida, summer; Caribbean Sea.

Fig. 65

Ceratium horridum Gran, 1902

Gran, 1902, p. 54, figs. 193-194; Schiller, 1937, p. 413, fig. 455a-c.

Small, short-horned, robust, variable; apical horn straight, toothed at base; antapicals with slightly concave base, projecting outward and curved forward, with wings and often teeth. Body length about 50 μ. Grades into *C. buceros*, f. *tenue*.

Cool-water form in Atlantic, Pacific, and Indian oceans. Rare in winter on Bahama Banks and in Santaren Channel, Straits of Florida.

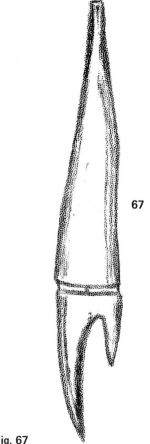

67

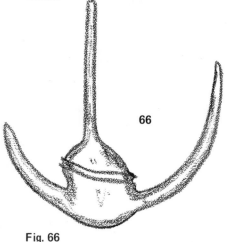

66

Fig. 66

Ceratium humile Jörgensen, 1911

Jörgensen, 1911, p. 40, figs. 82-83; Schiller, 1937, p. 390, fig. 428; Wood, 1954, p. 287, fig. 208.

Epitheca low, rounded; apical horn straight, short; hypotheca gibbous, low; left antapical short, regularly curved, directed obliquely

Fig. 67

Ceratium incisum (Karsten) Jörgensen, 1911

Jörgensen, 1911; *C. furca incisum* Karsten, 1906, pl. 23 (fig. 6a-b).

Epitheca very narrow, lanceolate, gradually tapering to near apex, then horn-shaped, bent slightly dorsally; hypotheca sides parallel, base angle large; antapicals very unlike, smooth, parallel, left twice as long and thick as right, bent dorsally and laterally, right horn thin, lanceolate; theca walls thickened dorsally. Length 100-180 μ.

Atlantic Ocean; Pacific and Indian oceans, tropical. Brazil (north coast).

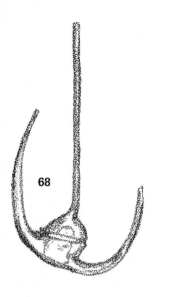

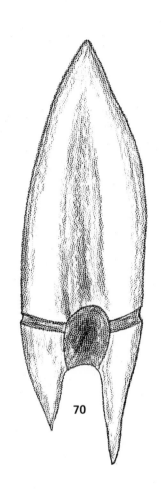

Fig. 68

Ceratium karsteni Pavillard, 1907

Pavillard, 1907, p. 152; Schiller, 1937, p. 393, fig. 431a-b; Wood, 1954, p. 289, fig. 211a-b.

A large species, similar in general shape to *C. tripos* but much more robust; theca almost triangular; apical horn curved slightly, long; base flat to convex; antapicals curving at base then straight, parallel to apical; right antapical bent toward apical near tip or twisted. Length 250-300 μ.

Tropical to subtropical form, frequent but not abundant in oceanic waters. Straits of Florida; Benguela Current; Brazil (north coast).

Fig. 69

Ceratium kofoidi Jörgensen, 1911

Jörgensen, 1911, p. 23, figs. 38-39; Schiller, 1937, p. 373, fig. 421a-b; Wood, 1954, p. 278, fig. 195.

A small species; epitheca high, sides straight to convex; apical horn straight, tapering; hypotheca about equal to epitheca, base acutely angled; antapicals directed straight back, sharply pointed, left twice as long as right. Body length 40-50 μ.

Tropical oceanic species, frequent but rarely abundant. Santaren Channel, West Channel, Straits of Florida; Bahama Banks; Benguela Current; Brazil (north coast); Caribbean Sea.

Fig. 70

Ceratium lanceolatum Kofoid, 1907

Kofoid, 1907b, p. 172, pl. 3 (fig. 17).

Body broadly lanceolate, sides parallel then tapering to acute apex; hypotheca low, base acute; antapical horns lanceolate, tapering evenly from girdle. Length 100-150 μ.

Pacific Ocean. Brazil (north coast)—new record from the Atlantic Ocean.

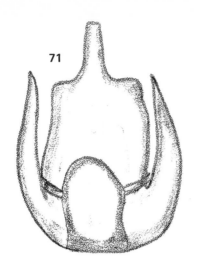

71

Fig. 71

Ceratium limulus Gourret, 1883

Gourret, 1883, p. 33, pl. 1 (fig. 7); Wood, 1954, p. 296, fig. 223a-b.

Body comparatively large, flattened, humps on each side of apical horn which is short, blunt, and tapered; base strongly rounded, merging forward into antapical horns which project almost entirely forward. Body may be strongly sculptured. Length 60 μ.

Interoceanic warm-water species. Straits of Florida; Brazil (north coast); Caribbean Sea.

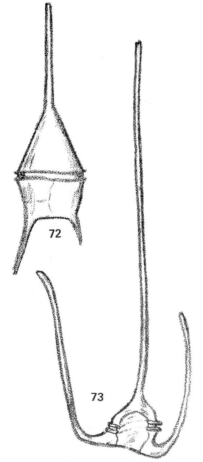

72

73

Fig. 72

Ceratium lineatum (Ehrenberg) Cleve, 1899

Cleve, 1899, p. 36; Schiller, 1937, p. 372, fig. 410; Wood, 1954, p. 277, fig. 192a-b.

A small species with triangular epitheca and tapering, blunt apical horn; hypotheca quadrate, sides tapering; antapical horns directed posteriorly at an angle, straight, tapering, closed. Body length 30-40 μ. Smaller than *C. pentagonum* and narrower in proportion.

Temperate and cold waters. Recorded by Hulburt (1963) from the Gulf Stream above 34° N.; this could be mistaken identity or due to upwelling.

Fig. 73

Ceratium longinum Karsten, 1906

Karsten, 1906, pl. 21, fig. 18a-b; Wood, 1954, p. 297, fig. 225.

Similar to *C. karsteni* and *C. contortum*. Graham and Bronkiowsky (1944) considered *C. longinum* a form of the latter. Apical horn long and slender, bent to left at base; epitheca low; base straight or slightly convex, merging into antapicals, which are bent forward and ventrally, and which may be wavy or straight, slender. Length about 600 μ.

Atlantic and Indian oceans, rare in the Pacific Ocean. Straits of Florida.

Fig. 74

Ceratium longipes (Bailey) Gran, 1902

Gran, 1902, p. 52, fig. 193; Schiller, 1937, p. 410, fig. 452a-c; Wood, 1954, p. 300; *Peridinium longipes* Bailey, 1855, p. 12.

Very like forms of *C. horridum* of which it is probably a variety; differs in curvature of apical horn and respective angles of antapicals; differs in like manner from *C. buceros.* Length 150-250 μ.

Cold water from North Sea, Baltic Sea, and south of subtropical convergence in sub-Antarctic waters. Recorded from the Gulf Stream south of 34° N. by Hulburt (1963).

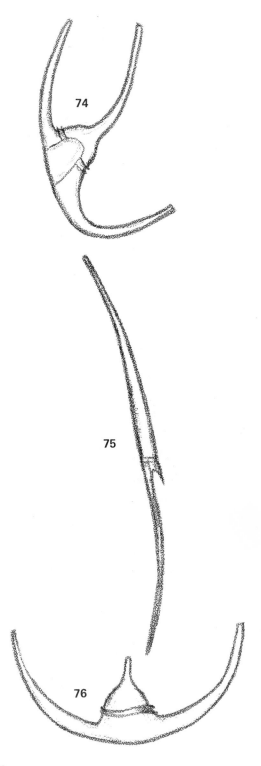

Fig. 75

Ceratium longirostrum Gourret, 1883

Gourret, 1883, p. 55, pl. 4 (fig. 65); Schiller, 1937, p. 376, fig. 416a-b; Wood, 1954, p. 281, figs. 199-200; *C. falcatum* (Kofoid) Jörgensen, 1920, p. 39, fig. 28.

There seems no reason to try to differentiate these two forms, of which *C. pennatum* formae are also synonyms. Epitheca long and narrow, tapering into bent apical horn; hypotheca shorter than epitheca; left antapical long, curved, thickened on concave side, blunt; right antapical short and needle-like. Length about 500 μ.

Interoceanic tropical species extending into subtropical waters. Santaren Channel, Straits of Florida; Benguela Current.

Fig. 76

Ceratium lunula Schimper, 1900

Schimper, in Chun, 1900, p. 73, fig. a; Schiller, 1937, p. 399, fig. 439a-b; Wood, 1954, p. 291, fig. 215a-b.

Epitheca almost triangular, low; hypotheca shorter than epitheca with faintly convex base; apical horn may be long in first cell of chain or in single cells or very short and stumpy in subsequent chain of cells; antapicals very long, evenly rounded from base to tip, which is closed. Length 100-150 μ.

Subtropical waters, oceanic. Straits of Florida; Caribbean Sea; Brazil (north coast).

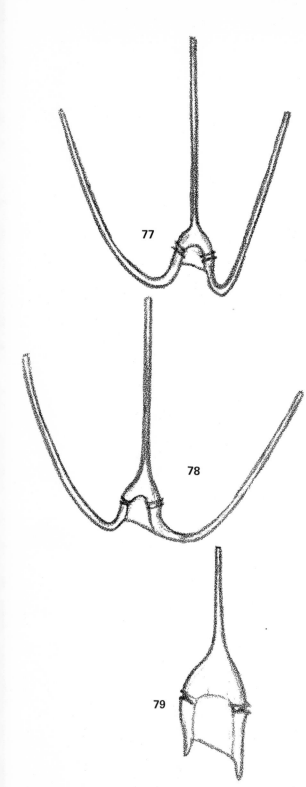

Fig. 77

Ceratium macroceros (Ehrenberg) Cleve, 1900

Cleve, 1900, p. 227; Schiller, 1937, p. 428, fig. 468; Wood, 1954, p. 310, fig. 238a.

Body small; apical horn slender, straight or slightly curved; antapicals pointing rearward then turning more or less forward. Body length 50-60 μ. Differs from *C. massiliense* var. *macroceroides* by being smaller and by the rearward direction of the bases of the antapicals; *C. gallicum* is much more slender and the body more rectangular.

Cool-water form, interoceanic. Gulf of Mexico (Curl, 1959)—Curl's diagram is *C. buceros,* so this is probably a misidentification; Amazon delta; Straits of Florida.

Fig. 78

Ceratium massiliense (Gourret) Jörgensen, 1911

Jörgensen, 1911, p. 66, figs. 140-142; Schiller, 1937, p. 422, fig. 463a-d; Wood, 1954, p. 306, fig. 235; *C. tripos* var. *massiliense* Gourret, 1883, p. 27.

Large, long-horned, very variable; epitheca oblique; base contour straight or slightly concave; apical long, straight; antapicals arising almost at right angles to each other, then bending sharply through a right angle and becoming straight or evenly curved with wavy or incurved ends. Body length 50-80 μ; total length variable.

Warm-water species, interoceanic. Straits of Florida; Benguela Current; Gulf of Mexico (Curl, 1959); Gulf Stream (Hulburt, 1962); Brazil (north coast); Caribbean Sea.

Fig. 79

Ceratium minutum Jörgensen, 1920

Jörgensen, 1920, p. 34, figs. 21-23; Schiller, 1937, p. 374, fig. 413a-c; Wood, 1954, p. 279, fig. 196.

A small species with rotund body and short horns; epitheca rounded, tapering sharply into short apical horn; hypotheca with angled base and short, closed antapicals directed backward. Body length 25-30 μ. More rotund and with shorter antapicals than *C. kofoidi.*

Straits of Florida; Gulf Stream (Hulburt, 1963); Benguela Current; Brazil (north coast).

Fig. 80

Ceratium paradoxides Cleve, 1900

Cleve, 1900, p. 15, pl. 7 (fig. 14); Wood, 1963*a*, p. 40, fig. 147.

Body comparatively large with two humps and short horns, all directed forward; base semicircular; theca with irregular polygonal markings as a characteristic. Length 80-150 μ.

Indian, Pacific, and Atlantic oceans in tropics. Straits of Florida; Caribbean Sea; Brazil (north coast).

Fig. 81

Ceratium pavillardi Jörgensen, 1911

Jörgensen, 1911, p. 74, figs. 157-158; Wood, 1954, p. 304, fig. 232a-b.

Epitheca almost triangular, tapering to a straight apical horn; hypotheca with base sharply at an angle to longitudinal axis; right antapical first transverse then bent sharply forward; left antapical directed backward then sharply forward at 30 to 50° with apical horn. Body length 80-100 μ. Close to *C. vultur,* but theca not so strongly thickened.

Warm-water, interoceanic species. Straits of Florida.

Fig. 82

Ceratium pentagonum Gourret, 1883

Gourret, 1883, p. 45, pl. 4 (fig. 58); Schiller, 1937, p. 370, fig. 408; Wood, 1954, p. 276, fig. 191a-f.

Very variable; body pentagonal, usually with clear plate sutures and surface thickenings; apical horn long or short (reduced in certain strains); antapicals short, thick, tapering. Body length 50-150 μ.

Eupelagic in all oceans. Bahama Banks; Santaren Channel, Straits of Florida; Tongue of the Ocean; Benguela Current; Gulf of Mexico (Curl, 1959); Gulf Stream and Sargasso Sea (Hulburt *et al.,* 1960; Hulburt, 1962; Hulburt and Rodman, 1963); Brazil (north coast); Caribbean Sea.

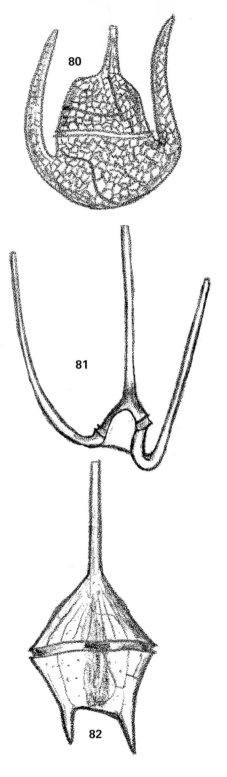

37

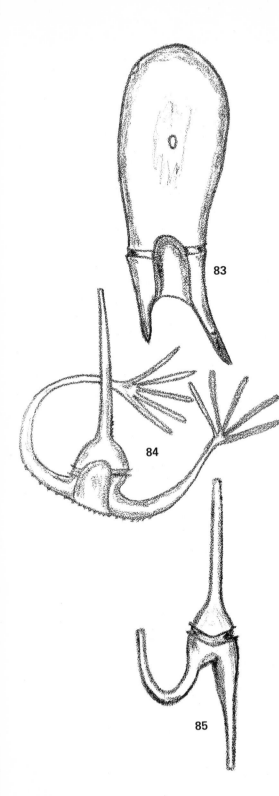

Fig. 83

Ceratium praelongum (Lemmermann) Kofoid, 1907

Kofoid, 1907b, p. 182; Schiller, 1937, p. 357, fig. 385; Wood, 1963a, p. 40, fig. 148; *C. gravidum* var. *praelongum* Lemmermann, 1900, p. 349.

Epitheca much larger than hypotheca, widening toward apex, sides almost parallel, rounded toward apex; apical horn absent; apical pore in upper third of epitheca; hypotheca narrower than epitheca, almost square; antapical horns strong, normally diverging, sometimes converging, directed posteriorly. Length 200 μ.

Rare tropical species, oceanic. West Channel, Straits of Florida; Benguela Current; Brazil (north coast); Caribbean Sea.

Fig. 84

Ceratium ranipes Cleve, 1900

Cleve, 1900, p. 15, pl. 7, fig. 1; Schiller, 1937, p. 409, fig. 451a; Wood, 1954, p. 299, fig. 227.

Small species with strong surface markings on theca; apical horn bent, winged; hypotheca triangular; right apical horn emerging at an angle of about 30° with apical horn, curving forward, approaching apical, with five to seven fingers at tip; left antapical also curved forward with fingers at tip. Body length 50-60 μ.

Tropical to subtropical, usually rare. Straits of Florida; Benguela Current.

Fig. 85

Ceratium reflexum Cleve, 1900

Cleve, 1900, p. 15, pl. 7 (figs. 8-9); Wood, 1954, p. 305; Wood, 1963a, p. 40, fig. 149.

Body small, tapering to short apical horn; hypotheca deep; left antapical horn directed straight backward, truncate; right antapical bending sharply forward, short. Length 100 μ.

Tropical Atlantic and Indian oceans, rare in Pacific Ocean. Straits of Florida; Brazil (north coast).

Fig. 86

Ceratium schmidti Jörgensen, 1911

Jörgensen, 1911, p. 50, figs. 110-111; Schiller, 1937, p. 400, fig. 44.

Large form with short antapicals; epitheca very high; hypotheca longer than epitheca; base continuous with both antapicals; apical horn long, slightly bent to left at base and widened with short, high wings; antapicals strongly recurved parallel to body, right antapical again bent dorsally at tip. Length 300 μ.

Pacific Ocean. Amazon canyon; Caribbean Sea.

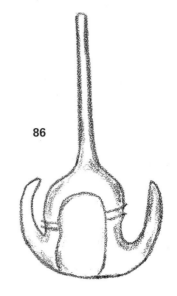

Fig. 87

Ceratium schroeteri Schröder, 1906

Schröder, 1906, p. 368, fig. 43; Wood, 1963a, p. 42, fig. 150.

Epitheca elongate, slightly twisted, ventral margin sigmoid, dorsal straight to slightly sigmoid, tapering to a fine point; hypotheca short; smaller antapical evenly tapering to a fine point; larger, much stronger and curved outward and posteriorly. Length about 300 μ.

Rare warm-water species; Mediterranean Sea; Pacific Ocean. Caribbean Sea and adjacent waters of the tropical Atlantic Ocean.

Fig. 88

Ceratium setaceum Jörgensen, 1911

Jörgensen, 1911, p. 23, figs. 40-41; Schiller, 1937, p. 373, fig. 411; Wood, 1954, p. 278, fig. 194a-b.

Body pentagonal, hyaline, flat but curved; apical slender, long, straight; antapicals short, evenly tapering, widely separated. Length about 300 μ.

Tropical oceanic species. West Channel, Straits of Florida; Benguela Current; Brazil (north coast); Caribbean Sea.

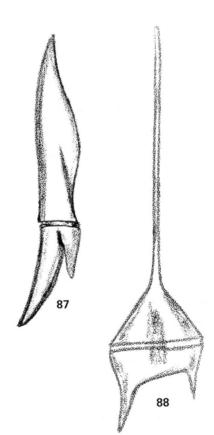

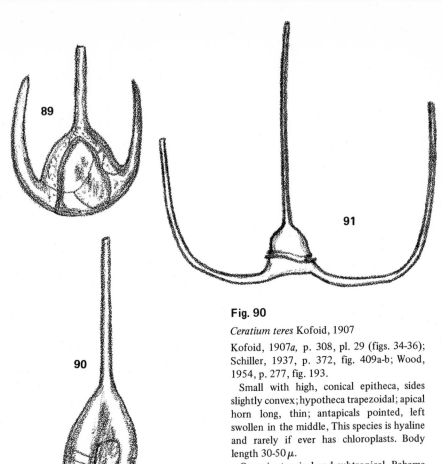

Fig. 90

Ceratium teres Kofoid, 1907

Kofoid, 1907*a*, p. 308, pl. 29 (figs. 34-36); Schiller, 1937, p. 372, fig. 409a-b; Wood, 1954, p. 277, fig. 193.

Small with high, conical epitheca, sides slightly convex; hypotheca trapezoidal; apical horn long, thin; antapicals pointed, left swollen in the middle, This species is hyaline and rarely if ever has chloroplasts. Body length 30-50 μ.

Oceanic, tropical and subtropical. Bahama Banks; Santaren Channel and West Channel, Straits of Florida; Benguela Current; Sargasso Sea and Bermuda (Hulburt, 1963); Brazil (north coast); Caribbean Sea.

Fig. 91

Ceratium trichoceros (Ehrenberg) Kofoid, 1908

Kofoid, 1908, p. 388; Schiller, 1937, p. 430, fig. 470; Wood, 1954, p. 311, fig. 239a; *Peridinium trichoceros* Ehrenberg, 1859, p. 791.

Body small; epitheca rounded; horns thin and long; antapicals beginning almost parallel to girdle, then curved until they are parallel with apical horn and almost the same length forming a flat-bottomed U. Length 300-500 μ.

Tropical and subtropical species, oceanic-neritic. Straits of Florida; Benguela Current; Gulf of Mexico (Curl, 1959); Sargasso Sea and Gulf Stream (Hulburt, 1963); Brazil (north coast); Caribbean Sea.

Fig. 89

Ceratium symmetricum Pavillard, 1905

Pavillard, 1905, p. 52, pl. 1 (fig. 4); Schiller, 1937, p. 401, fig. 441a-d; Wood, 1954, p. 292, fig. 217a-c.

Medium-sized, robust form, body much longer than broad, flattened; epitheca convex, steep toward apical horn, which may be straight or curved; antapicals continuous with slightly gibbous base, very symmetrically rounded, ends closed and incurved toward apical horn. Length 150-200 μ.

Warm-water interoceanic species. Straits of Florida; Benguela Current; Brazil (north coast); Caribbean Sea.

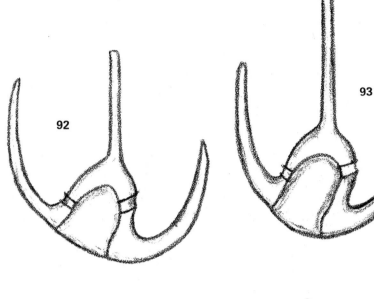

Fig. 92

Ceratium tripos (O. F. Müller) Nitzsch, 1817

Nitzsch, 1817, p. 4; Schiller, 1937, p. 382, figs. 384-385, 421a-e; Wood, 1954, p. 284, fig. 205a-c; *Cercaria tripos,* O. F. Müller, 1781, p. 206.

Epitheca rounded, plates usually apparent; apical horn long, even, slightly bent at base; antapicals more or less continuous with slightly flattened base, then sharply curved forward, parallel to or making an acute angle with apical horn. Body length 75-90 μ.

Cosmopolitan. Straits of Florida; Benguela Current; Gulf of Mexico (Curl, 1959); Brazil (Moreira, 1964); Caribbean Sea.

Fig. 93

Ceratium tripos var. *pulchellum* (Schröder) nov. comb.

Schröder, 1906, p. 358, fig. 27; Schiller, 1937, p. 386, figs. 422-423; Wood, 1954, p. 286, fig. 206.

Differs from the typical *C. tripos* in having a slightly gibbous base and evenly rounded antapical horns. Intergrades occur.

Straits of Florida, winter; Caribbean Sea.

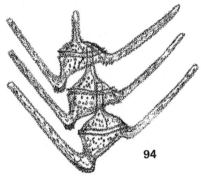

Fig. 94

Ceratium vultur Cleve, 1900

Cleve, 1900, p. 15, pl. 7 (fig. 5); Schiller, 1937, p. 418, fig. 459a-b; Wood, 1954, p. 304, fig. 233a.

Robust species with low, wide epitheca and triangular hypotheca;apical horn bent,strongly winged; left antapical horn starts at right angles to apical, turning sharply forward, diverging from or parallel to apical; right antapical directed backward at base, abruptly elbowed and turning forward at an angle or parallel to apical. Size variable.

Tropical to subtropical oceanic species; Mediterranean Sea (Kimor and Wood, MS.). Straits of Florida; Brazil (north coast).

Genus CERATOCORYS Stein

Body rounded or angular; epitheca and hypotheca often flattened distally, girdle anterior; fins well developed, surface smooth to rugose, coarsely pitted, with sheathed spines at junction of sutures, often sheathed; plate formula 3', 1a, 5'', 6''', 1p, 1''''.

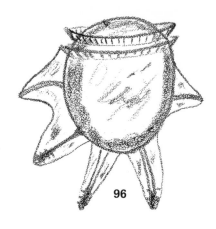

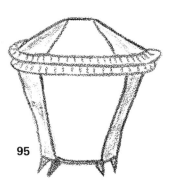

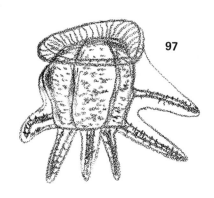

Fig. 95

Ceratocorys armata (Schütt) Kofoid, 1910

Kofoid, 1910, p. 181; Schiller, 1937, p. 444, fig. 486a-e; Wood, 1954, p. 314, fig. 243a-b; *Goniodoma acuminatum* var. *armatum* Schütt, 1895, p. 153.

Epitheca angular or rounded, shallow; plates well marked; hypotheca trapezoidal, plates marked; three or four short horns arising from rims or edges of hypothecal plates; girdle list ribbed; surface of theca porulate. Length 100 μ.

Straits of Florida; Benguela Current; Brazil (north coast); Caribbean Sea.

Fig. 96

Ceratocorys gourreti Paulsen, 1930

Paulsen, 1930, p. 38.

Body in side view rounded-oval, more or less constricted at sides; epitheca very low, rounded; hypotheca rotund; in sagittal plate arise five winged spines—two ventral, two basal, and one dorsal. Body length 80-100 μ. Resembles a *Phalacroma*.

Mediterranean Sea; Australian coast. Amazon basin.

Fig. 97

Ceratocorys horrida Stein, 1883

Stein, 1883, p. 20, pl. 6 (figs. 4-11); Schiller, 1937, p. 443, fig. 485a-c; Wood, 1954, p. 313, fig. 242a-b.

Variable species; body angular; epitheca low; ribs marked; hypotheca angular to rounded, deep; girdle lists strongly ribbed; strong toothed spines extending from corners of antapical plates, sometimes winged. Body length 80-120 μ.

Tropical oceanic species. Santaren Channel, Straits of Florida; Guinea and Benguela currents; Sargasso Sea (Hulburt, 1962); Brazil (north coast); Caribbean Sea.

Genus CITHARISTES Stein

Theca in side view C-shaped, posterior margin semicircular; girdle strongly anterior, similar to *Dinophysis;* anterior girdle list wide and flaring, ribbed; posterior list narrow; pouch present between lower part of body and girdle.

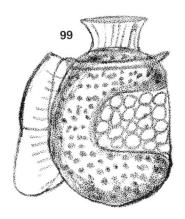

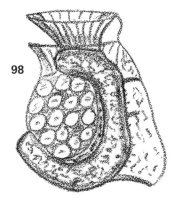

Genus CLADOPYXIS Stein

Body ovate to spherical; epitheca smaller than hypotheca and with apical pore; girdle deep, anterior; from the middle of the four epithecal and six hypothecal plates arise spines or processes which may be straight or branched; plate formula 4', Oa, 8'', 6''', 2''''.

Fig. 98

Citharistes apsteini Gräf, 1909

Gräf, 1909, p. 194; Wood, 1963*a*, pl. 22, fig. 67.

Body C-shaped; anterior girdle list widely funnel-shaped; posterior list narrow; girdle narrow; phaeosome chamber encasing body from lower part of the C to the posterior girdle list; sulcal lists even, left list ribbed, extending along ventral portion to base. Length 60-70 μ.

Tropical and subtropical oceans. Straits of Florida.

Fig. 99

Citharistes regius Stein, 1883

Stein, 1883, pl. 11 (figs. 1-4); Wood, 1963*b*, p. 8, fig. 20.

Body C-shaped, strongly porulate; anterior girdle list high, posterior list low, not as deep as girdle; left sulcal list widening posteriorly, rounded toward base, ribbed; phaeosome chamber reinforced dorsally. Length 40 μ.

Tropical and subtropical oceans; Coral Sea. Straits of Florida; Caribbean Sea.

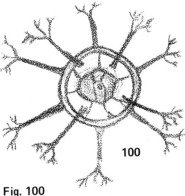

Fig. 100

Cladopyxis brachiolata Stein, 1883

Stein, 1883, p. 2, figs. 7-8; Wood, 1963*a*, p. 51, fig. 189.

Body oval; girdle premedian, narrow, circular, offset; sulcus small, elliptical; epitheca low, rounded, with four thick, repeatedly branched processes, each with an axial fiber; hypotheca rounded with six similar processes. Length 50 μ.

Tropical waters of oceans and seas; Mediterranean Sea (Kimor and Wood, MS.). Straits of Florida; Caribbean Sea.

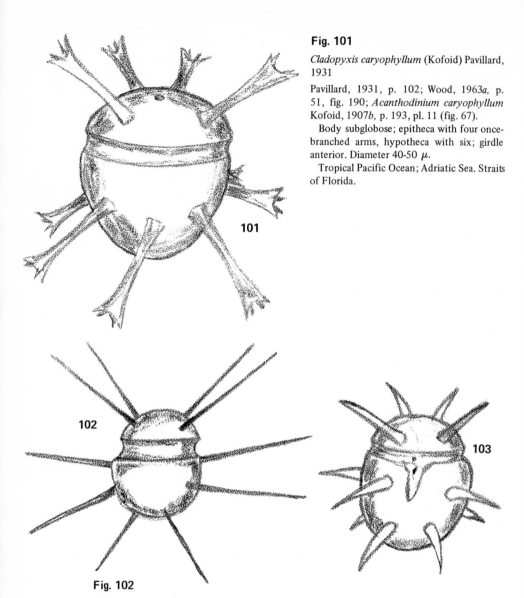

Fig. 101

Cladopyxis caryophyllum (Kofoid) Pavillard, 1931

Pavillard, 1931, p. 102; Wood, 1963*a*, p. 51, fig. 190; *Acanthodinium caryophyllum* Kofoid, 1907*b*, p. 193, pl. 11 (fig. 67).

Body subglobose; epitheca with four once-branched arms, hypotheca with six; girdle anterior. Diameter 40-50 μ.

Tropical Pacific Ocean; Adriatic Sea. Straits of Florida.

Fig. 102

Cladopyxis setifera Lohmann, 1902

Lohmann, 1902, p. 64, pl. 1 (fig. 15); Schiller, 1937, p. 468, fig. 537.

Body round-ovate, somewhat flattened dorsoventrally; epitheca shallower than hypotheca; girdle recessed, slightly anterior; four to five long, unbranched spines springing from epitheca, five to six from hypotheca. Body length 12-20 μ.

Baltic Sea; Adriatic Sea; Gulf of Naples. Sargasso Sea (Hulburt *et al.,* 1960; Hulburt, 1962).

Fig. 103

Cladopyxis spinosa (Kofoid) Schiller, 1937

Schiller, 1937, p. 469, fig. 538.

Body depressed, spherical; epitheca low, subconical with rounded sides; hypotheca much deeper; girdle anterior, slightly depressed; sulcus small, about half length of hypotheca; sculpture marked; spines short, strong and tapered, simple, four on epitheca, six on hypotheca. Length 40-50 μ.

Eastern Pacific Ocean. Straits of Florida.

Genus COCHLODINIUM Schütt

Cell naked, with body twisted at least one and one-half turns; girdle a descending spiral of at least one and one-half turns, widely displaced; sulcus with or without apical and antapical loops, also twisted.

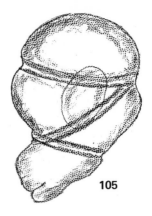

105

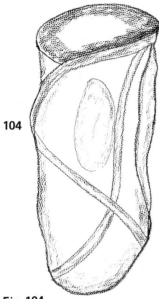

104

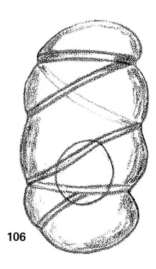

106

Fig. 104

Cochlodinium cavatum Kofoid and Swezy, 1921

Kofoid and Swezy, 1921, p. 356, pl. 9 (fig. 93).

Body elongate, strongly concave ventrally, convex dorsally; girdle forming a left spiral; sulcus arises near apex, forming a left spiral of half a turn, ending at the broad antapical invagination. Length 75 μ.

Pacific Ocean. Brazil (north coast).

Fig. 105

Cochlodinium constrictum (Schütt) Lemmermann, 1899.

Lemmermann, 1899, p. 360.

Body roughly biconical, with rounded apices; girdle anterior, forming a left spiral, and borne on a ridge; sulcus lies between the two high lists of the girdle running right around the cell and then longitudinally to base. Length 90 μ.

Atlantic Ocean; Mediterranean Sea. Brazil (north coast).

Fig. 106

Cochlodinium faurei Kofoid and Swezy, 1921

Kofoid and Swezy, 1921, p. 366, pl. 2 (fig. 25); Schiller, 1937, p. 526, fig. 555; Wood, 1963*a*, p. 33, fig. 116.

Body subovate to ellipsoidal; girdle a left spiral of two turns, much displaced; sulcus a spiral of about one and one-fifth turns with apical and antapical loops. Length 50-60 μ.

California coast; Coral Sea; Vitiaz Strait. Santaren Channel, West Channel, Straits of Florida; Benguela Current; Brazil (north coast).

Fig. 107

Cochlodinium pirum (Schütt) Lemmermann, 1899

Lemmermann, 1899, p. 360; Kofoid and Swezy, 1921, p. 374, text fig. GG3, pl. 9 (fig. 101); *Gymnodinium pirum* Schütt, 1895, p. 166, pl. 23, fig. 76.

Body ovate, flattened ventrally; epicone larger than hypocone, somewhat tapering with rounded apex; hypocone rounded; girdle one and one-half spiral; sulcus beginning near apex, increasingly curved to base. Length 60-85 μ.

Atlantic and Pacific oceans. Caribbean Sea; Brazil (north coast).

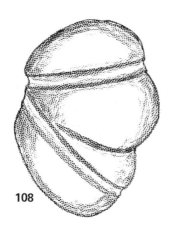

Fig. 108

Cochlodinium schuetti Kofoid and Swezy, 1921

Kofoid and Swezy, 1921, p. 380, text fig. HH2.

Body elliptical with rounded apices; girdle a left spiral of about one and one-half turns, depressed; sulcus beginning just above its junction with the girdle and forming a half-spiral to the base. Length 60-80 μ.

Pacific Ocean; Atlantic Ocean; Adriatic Sea. Brazil (north coast).

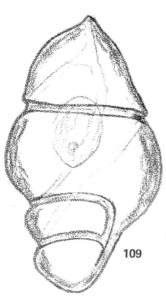

Fig. 109

Cochlodinium strangulatum Schütt, 1896

Schütt, 1896, pl. 5 (fig. 7); Kofoid and Swezy, 1921, p. 381, text fig. GG11, pl. 10 (fig. 113).

Body large, irregularly elliptical; apex broadly rounded; antapex rounded with a small protuberance; girdle forming a left-handed spiral of one and one-half turns; sulcus arising on epicone, also forming a spiral, ending at antapex. Length 200 μ.

Atlantic Ocean; Mediterranean Sea. Caribbean Sea.

Fig. 110

Cochlodinium virescens Kofoid and Swezy, 1921

Kofoid and Swezy, 1921, p. 386, text fig. HH11, pl. 9 (fig. 104).

Body ellipsoidal, nearly symmetrical; deeply constricted girdle a left spiral; sulcus twisted nearly one turn. Length 40-60 μ.

Pacific Ocean. Brazil (north coast); Caribbean Sea.

Genus DINOPHYSIS Ehrenberg

Cells compressed laterally, never wedge-shaped as in *Phalacroma;* epitheca small or almost rudimentary with obliquely set girdle lists, the upper list being almost funnel-shaped, projecting beyond epitheca and often strengthened by radial ribs; left sulcal list often strongly developed and porulate; hypotheca may have spines or protuberances.

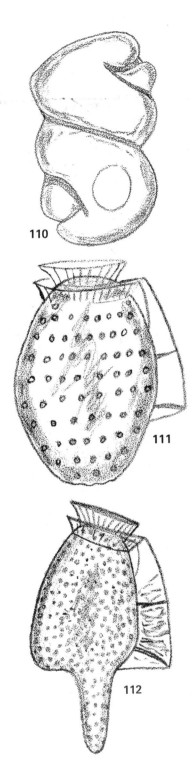

110

Fig. 111

Dinophysis acuminata Claparède and Lachmann, 1858-1861

Claparède and Lachmann, 1858-1861, p.408, pl. 20 (fig. 17); Schiller, 1933, p. 120, fig. 113a-g.

Cell elongate-oval, more or less symmetrical; epitheca very low, convex; hypotheca ovate or elliptical; antapex rounded with one or more protuberances; body coarsely pored; girdle lists with or without ribs; left sulcal list small, more than half body length and of even width; three main ribs well developed. Length 40-50 μ.

Shelf stations of Straits of Florida; Gulf Stream (Hulburt, 1963).

111

Fig. 112

Dinophysis caudata Saville-Kent, 1881

Saville-Kent, 1881, pp. 455, 460; Schiller, 1933, p. 153, fig. 145a-u; Wood, 1954, p. 201, fig. 49a-e.

Body very variable; epitheca low; hypotheca long, widest at or near the middle, anterior irregularly obovate, posterior portion rounded to angular, extending into a tapering process with rounded end; girdle list wide, ribbed; left sulcal list extending to base of peduncle, more or less reticulate. Length about 100 μ.

Tropical and subtropical estuarine-neritic species. Off Fowey Rocks; Cedar Key; Appalachee Bay (Curl, 1959).

112

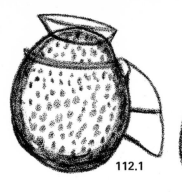

112.1

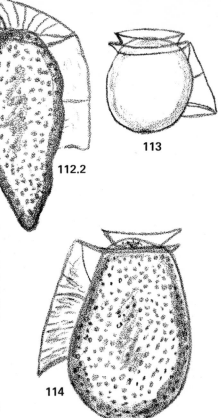

112.2

113

114

Fig. 112.1

Dinophysis dentata Schiller, 1928

Schiller, 1928, p. 75, fig. 35; Schiller, 1933, p. 115, fig. 107.

Body rotund; epitheca low, rounded; hypotheca round, even; girdle wide, anterior list hyaline, posterior list low; a small spine at the base of the right sulcal list distinguishes this species; left sulcal list ventral only, widening posteriorly, ending at third rib (R3). Length 25 μ.

Mediterranean Sea. Caribbean Sea.

Fig. 112.2

Dinophysis diegensis Kofoid, 1907

Kofoid, 1907*a*, p. 313, pl. 33 (fig. 57); Schiller, 1933, p. 151, fig. 114a-d.

Body elongate; epitheca low, higher dorsally; hypotheca tapering to base from about halfway, margins more or less irregular; theca porulate; left sulcal list more or less even in width, extending along one-half to two-thirds of ventral margin. Length about 100 μ. This species intergrades with *D. tripos* and *D. caudata* (see Wood, 1954).

California coast; Sydney Harbor. Biscayne Bay.

Fig. 113

Dinophysis exigua Kofoid and Skogsberg, 1928

Kofoid and Skogsberg, 1928, p. 239, fig. 30; Wood, 1963*a*, p. 6, fig. 12.

Body in lateral view circular to subcircular; epitheca low, not above anterior girdle list, which is hyaline and rather narrow; posterior list narrow; left sulcal list widest at R3 which is inclined posteriorly. Length 30-40 μ.

Tropical Pacific Ocean. Santaren Channel, Northwest Providence Channel, Straits of Florida; Atlantic Ocean (Bahamas); Brazil (north coast); Caribbean Sea.

Fig. 114

Dinophysis fortii Pavillard, 1923

Pavillard, 1923, p. 881; Schiller, 1933, p. 134, fig. 127a-c; Wood, 1954, p. 198, fig. 45.

Body narrowly subovate with flattened ventral margin, broadly and evenly rounded posteriorly, widest behind the middle; epitheca low, convex to flat; anterior girdle list twice as wide as girdle, may or may not be ribbed; left sulcal list straight, even, about three-quarters of body length, usually reticulate. Length 50-70 μ.

Warm-water neritic species, interoceanic. Pigeon Key; Gulf Stream (Hulburt, 1963).

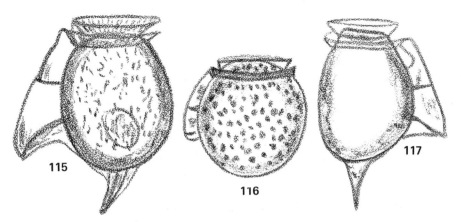

115

116

117

Fig. 115

Dinophysis hastata Stein, 1883

Stein, 1883, pl. 19 (fig. 12); Schiller, 1933, p. 138, fig. 131a-n; Wood, 1954, p. 199, fig. 47a-b.

Body subovate to ovate, rounded posteriorly; epitheca convex, low; hypotheca round, widest near middle; girdle list may be ribbed; left sulcal list widening to R3 which curves rearward; triangular hyaline posterior sail at, or slightly ventral to, longitudinal axis. Length 50-100 μ.

Warm-water neritic species. Straits of Florida; Brazil (north coast); Caribbean Sea.

Fig. 116

Dinophysis micropterygia Dangeard, 1927

Dangeard, 1927, p. 381, fig. 44e; Schiller, 1933, p. 110, fig. 101.

Body circular in lateral view; epitheca very low; hypotheca circular, constricted laterally; anterior girdle list about as wide as girdle; posterior list narrow; sulcal list very narrow and even, reaching about halfway to base of hypotheca. Length 50-60 μ.

Warm Atlantic waters. Caribbean Sea.

Fig. 117

Dinophysis monacantha Kofoid and Skogsberg, 1928

Kofoid and Skogsberg, 1928, p. 283, fig. 37 (2-3).

Body rounded-trapezoidal, widest below the middle; epitheca widest dorsally; anterior girdle list higher than epitheca, hyaline; posterior list hyaline; left sulcal list with straight margin widening toward R3, which is directed

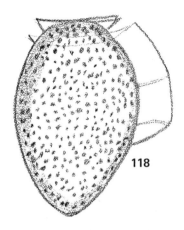

118

at about 60° to the longitudinal axis; a single unribbed posterior spine. Length 70 μ.

Eastern tropical Pacific Ocean. Caribbean Sea.

Fig. 118

Dinophysis norvegica Claparède and Lachmann, 1858-1861

Claparède and Lachmann, 1858-1861, p. 407, pl. 20 (fig. 19); Schiller, 1933, p. 128, fig. 122a-n.

Body ovate to cuneate; epitheca low; hypotheca widest near middle, more or less tapering with or without antapical protuberances; surface porulate, frequently with porulate extension at plate junction; girdle ribs narrow; sulcal list variable, may be reticulate. Length 60 μ.

Northern Atlantic Ocean. Gulf Stream (Hulburt, 1963).

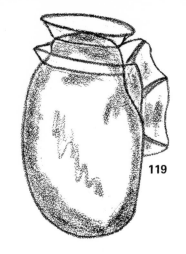

Fig. 119

Dinophysis okamurai Kofoid and Skogsberg, 1928

Kofoid and Skogsberg, 1928, p. 250, pl. 31 (fig. 5); Wood, 1954, p. 196, fig. 40.

Body subovate, with dorsal, shoulder-like constriction at girdle; ventral margin somewhat concave between R_2 and R_3; anterior girdle list about as wide as girdle; hypotheca somewhat asymmetrical, wider posteriorly; left sulcal list small, decreasing suddenly behind the posterior main rib. Length 40-50 μ.

Pacific Ocean; estuarine. Straits of Florida.

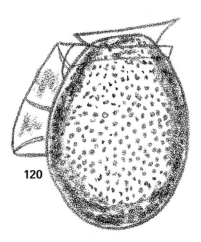

Fig. 120

Dinophysis ovum Schütt, 1895

Schütt, 1895, pl. 1 (fig. 6); Schiller, 1933, p. 116, fig. 109; Wood, 1954, p. 194, fig. 35a-d.

Body somewhat irregularly oval, asymmetrical; apex narrower than antapex, which is broadly rounded; dorsal contour more strongly convex than ventral; girdle lists ribbed or not; left sulcal list of even width, about one-half of body length; ribs of equal length; theca porulate. Length 45-65 μ.

Subtropical in northern hemisphere. West Channel, Straits of Florida; Sargasso Sea; Bermuda (Hulburt *et al.,* 1960; Hulburt, 1963); Benguela Current; Brazil (north coast); Caribbean Sea.

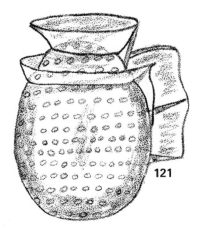

Fig. 121

Dinophysis parva Schiller, 1928

Schiller, 1928, p. 77, fig. 39; Wood, 1963*a*, p. 7, fig. 15.

Body regularly ovate; anterior girdle list as broad as or slightly narrower than girdle, recurved; posterior list narrow; left sulcal list about one-half of body length, curved, wider near R_3. Length 20-25 μ.

Adriatic and Coral seas. Straits of Florida; Caribbean Sea.

Fig. 122

Dinophysis punctata Jörgensen, 1923

Jörgensen, 1923, p. 23, fig. 28; Schiller, 1933, p. 118, fig. 111.

Body rotundly ovate; epitheca convex; anterior girdle list high, posterior low; body symmetrical about longitudinal axis; left sulcal list moderately wide, even but angular; ribs equal in length. Length 25-40 μ. Differs from *D. ovum* mainly in symmetry.

Warm- and cold-water species. Sargasso Sea (Hulburt, 1962).

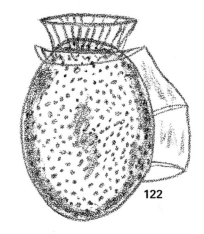

122

Fig. 123

Dinophysis recurva Kofoid and Skogsberg, 1928

Kofoid and Skogsberg, 1928, p. 228; Wood, 1963a, p. 7, fig. 16.

Body ovate; epitheca very small; upper girdle list about half cell diameter in height, slight depression between upper and lower girdle lists; sulcal list slightly more than half cell length; ribs curved posteriorly; body strongly areolate. Length 40-50 μ.

Mediterranean, Adriatic, and Coral seas; Atlantic Ocean. Straits of Florida.

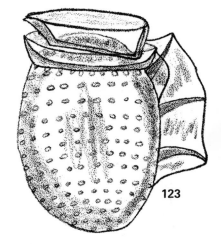

123

Fig. 124

Dinophysis sacculus Stein, 1883

Stein, 1883, pl. 20 (fig. 10); Wood, 1954, p. 199, fig. 46.

Body asymmetrical, variable; margins of hypotheca undulate, cell often more or less reniform; epitheca low, flat; anterior girdle list moderately wide; posterior list about equal to girdle; sulcal list of even width, extending slightly past R_3 which is situated about midbody; theca porulate; some protuberances may occur on ventral side of base. Length 50-60 μ.

Mediterranean Sea; Atlantic, Indian, and Pacific oceans. Straits of Florida.

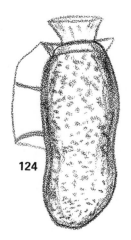

124

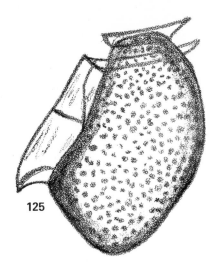

Fig. 125

Dinophysis schroederi Pavillard, 1909

Pavillard, 1909, p. 284, fig. 5; Wood, 1954, p. 198, fig. 44.

Body elongate, deepest behind the middle, nearly twice as long as broad, dorsal margin rotund, ventral margin slightly concave; surface porulate; anterior girdle list moderate; left sulcal list wide, margin straight, almost as long as body, often sculptured. Length 70-90 μ.

Interoceanic warm-water species. Straits of Florida.

Fig. 126

Dinophysis schuetti Murray and Whitting, 1899

Murray and Whitting, 1899, p. 331, pl. 31 (fig. 10); Schiller, 1933, p. 147, fig. 140a-e; Wood, 1963a, p. 7, fig. 17.

Body almost spherical to elliptical; epitheca very low; hypotheca widest behind middle; anterior girdle list high, ribbed; left sulcal list wide, extended by R_2 and R_3 which are approximate to body width; sail supported by an equally long rib arising slightly dorsally of longitudinal axis. Length 30-60 μ.

Santaren Channel, Straits of Florida; Benguela Current; Brazil (north coast); Caribbean Sea.

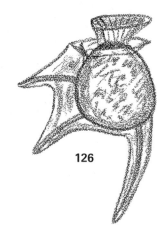

Fig. 127

Dinophysis similis Kofoid and Skogsberg, 1928

Kofoid and Skogsberg, 1928, p. 247, fig. 31; Wood, 1954, p. 196, fig. 39.

Body subcircular to ovate, deepest at or just behind the middle; epitheca slightly convex; hypotheca somewhat asymmetrical; anterior girdle list wider than girdle; left sulcal list about half body length, uniformly narrow, rounded posteriorly; posterior main rib absent or rudimentary. Length 45-60 μ.

Tropical or subtropical species. Straits of Florida.

Fig. 128

Dinophysis sphaerica Stein, 1883

Stein, 1883, pl. 20 (figs. 3-4); Schiller, 1933, p. 117, fig. 110a-e.

Body oval to ellipsoidal, widest somewhat below middle; epitheca rounded; hypotheca usually symmetrical; anterior girdle list high, ribbed; posterior list moderate; girdle wide; left sulcal list evenly wide, ending just behind R3, may be reticulate. Length 45-50 μ.

Amazon delta; Caribbean Sea.

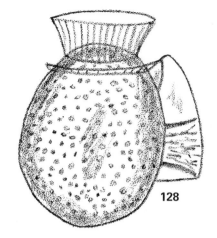

128

Fig. 129

Dinophysis tripos Gourret, 1883

Gourret, 1883, p. 114, pl. 3 (fig. 53); Schiller, 1933, p. 159, fig. 146a-g; Wood, 1954, p. 202, fig. 51a-c.

Body elongate, asymmetrical with low, almost flat epitheca; hypotheca irregular in contour with a large tapering antapical process, straight ventral margin, and dorsal margin extending into a second, smaller process; anterior girdle list high, tipped; left sulcal list evenly wide, often reticulate, extending to base of process. Length 100 μ. Intergrades with *D. caudata*.

Recorded by Curl (1959) from west coast of Florida, but illustration suggests an angular form of *D. caudata*. Straits of Florida; Caribbean Sea.

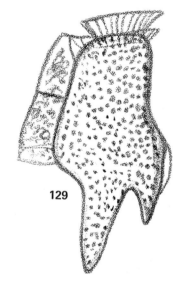

129

Fig. 130

Dinophysis umbosa Schiller, 1928

Schiller, 1928, pp. 77-78, pl. 3 (fig. 5); Schiller, 1933, p. 115, fig. 108.

Body broadly oval, slightly more convex on dorsal side; epitheca very low and flat; anterior girdle list moderate, ribbed; posterior list narrow; girdle much wider than posterior list; left sulcal list even, ending at the straight R3; body porulate with small blunt spinules. Length 25-30 μ.

Adriatic Sea. Straits of Florida.

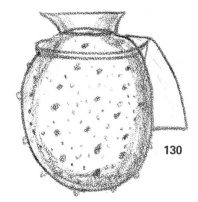

130

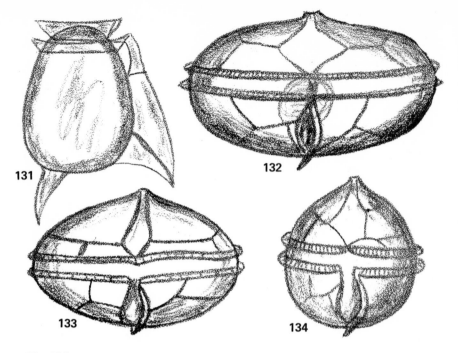

131 **132**

133 **134**

Fig. 131

Dinophysis uracantha Stein, 1883

Stein, 1883, figs. 22-23; Schiller, 1933, p. 142, fig. 134a-f; Wood, 1954, p. 200, fig. 48a-b.

Body subcircular to subovate; epitheca flat or convex; girdle list moderately wide; left sulcal list triangular, R_2 small, R_3 over half of body width, and curved posteriorly; strong spine on posterior margin, dorsally to longitudinal axis. Length 40-60 μ.

Warmer waters of all oceans. Straits of Florida; Brazil (north coast); Caribbean Sea.

Genus DIPLOPSALIS Bergh

Cell lenticular to subspherical, with hyaline, ribbed girdle lists and conspicuous left sulcal list extending beyond antapex; apical pore on apical horn; girdle not displaced, spines absent; plate formula 3-4', 1a, 2a, 6-7", 5''', 1-2''''.

Fig. 132

Diplopsalis lenticula Bergh, 1882

Bergh, 1882, figs. 60-62; Wood, 1954, p. 222, fig. 86a-c.

Cells lenticular, epitheca and hypotheca equal, margins convex; girdle almost central, not displaced, supported by fine spines; sulcus

usually reaching antapex; left side with prominent hyaline list; plate formula 3', 1a, 6", 5''', 1''''. Length 30-80 μ.

Cosmopolitan. West Channel, Straits of Florida; Benguela Current; Brazil (north coast); Florida Everglades; Caribbean Sea.

Fig. 133

Diplopsalis minor (Paulsen), 1907

Diplopsalis lenticula f. *minor* Paulsen, 1907.

Cell spherical, epitheca and hypotheca equal; girdle central, not displaced; lists evident, hyaline, ribbed; sulcus rounded at base, winged; plate formula 4', 1a, 7", 5''', 1''''. Length 30-60 μ.

Brazil (north coast); Caribbean Sea.

Fig. 134

Diplopsalis rotunda (Lebour) Wood, 1954

Wood, 1954, p. 223, fig. 88a-b; *Peridiniopsis rotunda* Lebour, 1922, p. 804, figs. 16, 20.

Cell globular, tapering to a very short apical horn; girdle central, not displaced; lists conspicuous, spined; plate formula 3', 1a, 6", 5''', 2''''. Length 20-30 μ.

Estuarine species from Plymouth Sound, (England), Swan River and Port Hacking (Australia). Straits of Florida.

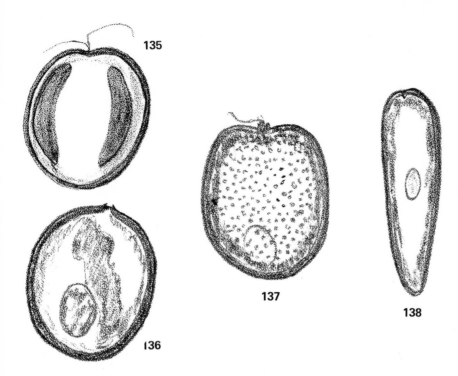

135

137

138

136

Genus EXUVIAELLA Cienkowski

Cell subspherical or oval, without anterior projection; theca with two lateral plates and a third plate joining these; two anterior flagella.

Fig. 135

Exuviaella apora Schiller, 1918

Schiller, 1918, p. 258, fig. 12a-b; Schiller, 1933, p. 19, fig. 14.

Body broadly oval, almost cylindrical, strongly constricted laterally; test symmetrical and thick; pores absent, chromatophores two. Length 30 μ.

Adriatic Sea; Plymouth. Caribbean Sea; Amazon River.

Fig. 136

Exuviaella baltica Lohmann, 1908

Lohmann, 1908, p. 17, pl. 1 (fig. 265); Schiller, 1933, p. 17, fig. 10a-d; Wood, 1963a, p. 4, fig. 1.

Body variable in shape, rotund to ovate, symmetrical or asymmetrical, only slightly constricted dorsoventrally; flagellar pore with a slight tooth on either side. Length 10-20 μ.

Neritic. Santaren Channel, bank and mid-channel of Straits of Florida; Sargasso Sea; Bermuda (Hulburt, 1963); Benguela Current; Brazil (north coast); Caribbean Sea.

Fig. 137

Exuviaella compressa Ostenfeld, 1899

Ostenfeld, 1899, p. 59; Schiller, 1937, p. 17, fig. 11a-d; Wood, 1954, p. 178, fig. 2.

Cell oval, much compressed; each valve with a very small tooth near the exit of the flagella; theca covered with conspicuous poroids. Length 30-50 μ.

Straits of Florida; Gulf of Mexico (Curl, 1959); Caribbean Sea.

Fig. 138

Exuviaella dactylus (Stein) Schütt, 1895

Schütt, 1895; *Dinopyxis dactylus* Stein, 1883, pl. 1 (figs. 20-23).

Body elongate, both ends rounded, posterior slightly narrower; anterior spine absent; flagellar pore small. Length 65-70 μ.

Atlantic Ocean. Northwest Providence Channel, Straits of Florida.

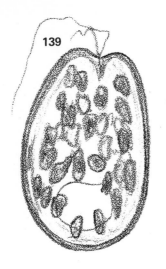

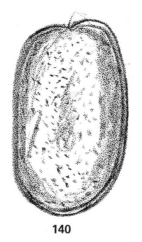

139

141

140

Fig. 139

Exuviaella marina Cienkowski, 1881

Cienkowski, 1881, p. 157, figs. 36-37; Schiller, 1933, p. 20, fig. 15; Wood, 1954, p. 178, fig. 1.

Cell oval, broadest behind middle, much compressed laterally; front of both valves indented, without spines; theca finely porulate. Length 35-50 μ.

Neritic-estuarine species, planktonic or epontic. Santaren Channel, Straits of Florida; Key Largo; Gulf Stream (Hulburt, 1963); Brazil (north coast); Caribbean Sea.

Fig. 140

Exuviaella oblonga Schiller, 1928

Schiller, 1928, p. 50, fig. 6a-c; Schiller, 1933, p. 22, fig. 17a-c.

Body elliptical, apex and base evenly rounded; flagellar pore concave; surface porulate. Length 30-40 μ.

Adriatic Sea. Straits of Florida.

Fig. 141

Exuviaella vaginula (Stein) Schütt, 1895

Schütt, 1895; Schiller, 1933, p. 24, fig. 21a-b; *Dinopyxis vaginula* Stein, 1883, pl. 1 (fig. 24).

Body pear-shaped with rounded anterior, acutely pointed posterior; valves porulate, no spinule; flagellar pore round. Length 30-40 μ.

Atlantic Ocean; Mediterranean Sea. Straits of Florida.

Genus GONIAULAX Diesing

Also spelled *Gonyaulax*. Theca variable in shape but epitheca and hypotheca subequal; girdle left-handed, displaced from one-half to seven times its width; sulcus occupies the whole ventral area; first apical plate narrow and even, extending from girdle to apex; sporulating *Goniaulax* dehisces along this plate and spore usually escapes anteriorly; plate formula 3-5', 0-2a, 6", 6''', 1p, 1''''.

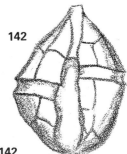

142

Fig. 142

Goniaulax apiculata (Penard) Entz, 1904

Entz, 1904, p. 12, fig. 4; Wood, 1954; *Peridinium apiculatum* Penard, 1891, p. 51, pl. 3 (figs. 3, 13).

Cell ovate; epitheca tapering to a short apical horn; hypotheca rounded, without spines; girdle depressed, displaced about one width, no lists; sulcus rounded, not reaching base. Length 30-65 μ.

In fresh and brackish water. Straits of Florida; Brazil (north coast); Caribbean Sea.

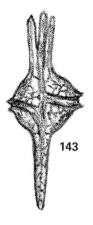

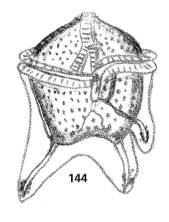

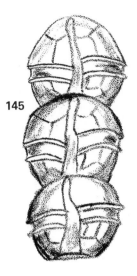

145

Fig. 143

Goniaulax birostris Stein, 1883

Stein, 1883, pl. 4 (fig. 20); Schiller, 1937, p. 300, fig. 308; Wood, 1954, p. 258, fig. 163.

Body spindle-shaped; epitheca and hypotheca rounded, equal, both extended into processes about equal to the length of the body; girdle depressed, offset about one and one-half widths. Length 100-150 μ. The illustrations of *G. glyptorhynchus* and *G. highleyi* by Murray and Whitting (1899) suggest that these are empty theca, probably of *G. birostris*.

Straits of Florida; Benguela Current; Brazil (north coast); Caribbean Sea.

Fig. 144

Goniaulax ceratocoroides Kofoid, 1910

Kofoid, 1910, p. 182; Wood, 1963*b*, p. 13, fig. 47.

Epitheca shallow-conical; plates separated by coarsely thickened ridges; hypotheca larger, five-sided; plates divided by strong ridges which are extended into curved and thickened horns supporting wings; girdle lists strongly ribbed; sulcus with numerous rows of pores. Length 50-60 μ.

Tropical Atlantic Ocean; Mediterranean Sea; Coral Sea. Straits of Florida.

Fig. 145

Goniaulax conjuncta Wood, 1954

Wood, 1954, p. 258, fig. 161.

Cells in short chains, polyhedral with rounded angles; epitheca and hypotheca subequal, flattened; antapex of basal cell slightly indented; girdle depressed, displaced about one-half width; sulcus shallow, flaring. Length of cell 25 μ.

Port Hacking (Australia); Zanzibar. Straits of Florida.

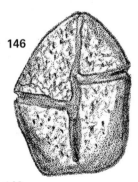

146

Fig. 146

Goniaulax dangeardi (Dangeard) Schiller, 1937

Schiller, 1937, p. 281, fig. 284; *Goniaulax pavillardi* Dangeard, 1927, p. 340, fig. 6b-c; non Kofoid and Michener, 1911.

Theca pentagonal; epitheca conical with convex sides; girdle depressed, displaced about two widths; hypotheca subrectangular; sulcus narrow, not reaching antapex, slightly sigmoid; surface strongly marked, sutures clear. Length 100 μ.

Atlantic Ocean in warm water.

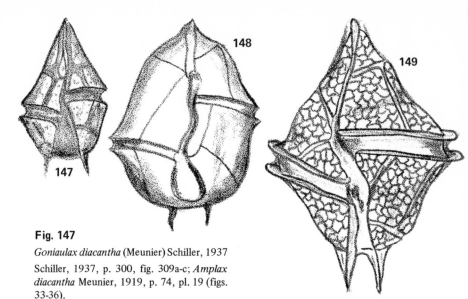

Fig. 147

Goniaulax diacantha (Meunier) Schiller, 1937

Schiller, 1937, p. 300, fig. 309a-c; *Amplax diacantha* Meunier, 1919, p. 74, pl. 19 (figs. 33-36).

Epitheca conical with slightly concave sides; girdle depressed, displaced about two widths; hypotheca subrotund, sides convex, base flattened; sulcus triangular, broadening to base; two strong antapical spines. Length 25 μ.

Belgium (in brackish water). Straits of Florida; Caribbean Sea.

Fig. 148

Goniaulax diegensis Kofoid, 1911

Kofoid, 1911a, p. 217, pl. 13 (figs. 21-24); Schiller, 1937, p. 281, fig. 285a-i.

Body rotund; apical horn short and stout; two or three antapical horns, all short; girdle depressed, little overhang, displaced about two widths; sulcus not abruptly widened opposite distal end of girdle. Length 65-100 μ.

English Channel; Atlantic Ocean; California coast. Santaren Channel, Straits of Florida; Benguela Current, Brazil (north coast).

Fig. 149

Goniaulax digitale (Pouchet) Kofoid, 1911

Kofoid, 1911a, p. 214, pl. 9 (figs. 1-5); Wood, 1954; *Protoperidinium digitale* Pouchet, 1883, p. 443, pls. 18-19 (fig. 14).

Epitheca subconical with irregular margins, tapering to apical horn; girdle depressed and flared, displaced about three widths and overlapping; sulcus triangular, reaching antapex;

two to four antapical spines. Length 50-75 μ. It is probable that this species, *G. spinifera*, *G. polygramma,* and *G. diegensis* are ecoforms of one species.

Estuarine, cosmopolitan species. Straits of Florida; Caribbean Sea.

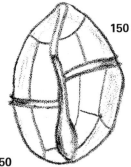

Fig. 150

Goniaulax fragilis (Schütt) Kofoid, 1911

Kofoid, 1911a, p. 248, pl. 15 (figs. 33-34, 36-37); Schiller, 1937, p. 305.

Body rotund, somewhat elongated, ventrally flattened; epitheca and hypotheca subequal; no apical horn; hypotheca abruptly rounded, asymmetrical; girdle slightly premedian, displaced three widths, without overhang, shallow; lists absent; sulcus widening posteriorly. Length 80-100 μ.

Atlantic and Pacific oceans; Mediterranean Sea. Brazil (north coast); Caribbean Sea.

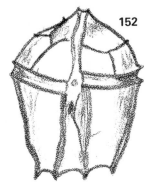

152

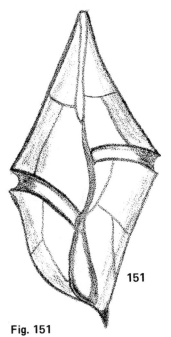

151

153

Fig. 153

Goniaulax minima Matzenauer, 1933

Matzenauer, 1933, p. 450, fig. 17; Schiller, 1937, p. 287, fig. 291; Wood, 1954, p. 264, fig. 179.

A minute species; body oval or suboval, tapering anteriorly; girdle displaced about one-half of its width, not or only slightly overlapping; sulcus nearly straight, widened posteriorly, not reaching antapex; antapex rounded, without spines. Length 20-30 μ.

Indian Ocean; Port Hacking (Australia). Straits of Florida; Caribbean Sea.

Fig. 151

Goniaulax kofoidi Pavillard, 1909

Pavillard, 1909, p. 271, fig. 1; Schiller, 1937, p. 285, fig. 288; Wood, 1954, p. 260, fig. 168a-c.

A large species with elongated body, tapering apical horn, asymmetrical antapex, and prominent left antapical spine; surface coarsely porulate, longitudinally striate; girdle section subcircular, flattened ventrally, girdle displaced two widths, not overlapping; hypotheca lower than epitheca. Length 100-150 μ.

Atlantic Ocean; Mediterranean Sea; California coast; Indian Ocean; Southwest Pacific Ocean. Benguela Current; Brazil (north coast; Providence channels, Straits of Florida.

Fig. 152

Goniaulax milneri Murray and Whitting, 1899

Murray and Whitting, 1899, p. 325, fig. 2a-d; Wood, 1963a, p. 37, fig. 133.

Epitheca rounded with tapering apical horn; girdle depressed, displaced about one width; hypotheca almost rectangular, with slight basal spines at the end of each raised suture; sulcus depressed, extending into epitheca. Length 40 μ.

Atlantic Ocean. Tropical waters including the western Caribbean Sea.

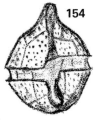

154

Fig. 154

Goniaulax minuta Kofoid and Michener, 1911

Kofoid and Michener, 1911, p. 271; Schiller, 1937, p. 287.

Theca almost spherical with a slightly tapering apical horn and apex; hypotheca almost hemispherical; girdle depressed, displaced about one width, sulcus only on hypotheca, rounded toward antapex; no spines or lists. Length 20-25 μ.

Warm waters of the eastern Pacific Ocean. Straits of Florida.

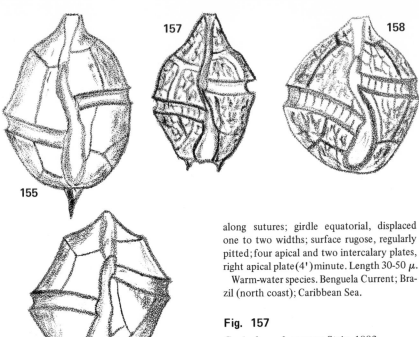

157

158

155

156

Fig. 155

Goniaulax monacantha Pavillard, 1916

Pavillard, 1916, p. 21, pl. 1 (fig. 78); Schiller, 1937, p. 287, fig. 293; Wood, 1954, p. 260, fig. 169a-b.

Cell polyhedral; epitheca irregularly conical, asymmetrically tapering into apical horn; hypotheca smaller than epitheca, sharply truncated at right, with one winged, well-developed spine; girdle strongly hollowed, edges somewhat protruding, no membrane, displaced at least three times width; theca coarsely porulate, mostly in rows. Length 35-60 μ.

Mediterranean Sea; Australian estuaries. Bahama Banks; West Channel, Santaren Channel, Straits of Florida; Benguela Current; Brazil (north coast); Caribbean Sea.

Fig. 156

Goniaulax polyedra Stein, 1883

Stein, 1883, p. 13, pl. 4, figs. 7-9; Schiller, 1937, p. 291, fig. 299a-f; Wood, 1954, p. 261, fig. 171a-b.

Body small, angular, polyhedral with ridges

along sutures; girdle equatorial, displaced one to two widths; surface rugose, regularly pitted; four apical and two intercalary plates, right apical plate (4') minute. Length 30-50 μ.

Warm-water species. Benguela Current; Brazil (north coast); Caribbean Sea.

Fig. 157

Goniaulax polygramma Stein, 1883

Stein, 1883, pl. 4 (fig. 15); Schiller, 1937, p. 292, fig. 300a-j; Wood, 1954, p. 261, fig. 172a-c.

Medium-sized species; ovate body; epitheca somewhat conical, tapering into a small, blunt apical horn; hypotheca subconical, with one to several antapical spines or ridges; girdle depressed, ridges narrow, displaced one to two widths, not overlapping; sulcus widening to base; surface of theca with longitudinal lines and pores, or reticulate. Length 40-60 μ.

Cosmopolitan. Bahama Banks; Santaren Channel, Straits of Florida; Brazil (north coast); Caribbean Sea.

Fig. 158

Goniaulax scrippsae Kofoid, 1911

Kofoid, 1911a, pp. 288-289, pl. 13 (figs. 26-27); Schiller, 1937, p. 295, fig. 303a-d.

Body sphaeroidal; girdle median, displaced two to three widths, indented and ridged; apical horn short with oblique apex; sulcus deep, sigmoid, rather narrow, end rounded; antapicals absent; theca with fine subparallel lines and may be punctate or reticulate. Length 30-50 μ.

Atlantic, Pacific, and Indian oceans; Mediterranean Sea. Brazil (north coast); Caribbean Sea.

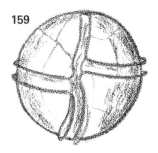

Fig. 159

Goniaulax sphaeroidea Kofoid, 1911

Kofoid, 1911a, p. 206, pl. 16 (figs. 41-42).

Theca spherical, surface smooth, no apical horn; girdle equatorial, not depressed; lists broad, hyaline; sulcus not reaching base, slightly curved, with lists on both sides. Length 45-50 μ.

California coast. Rare in Providence channels, Straits of Florida.

Fig. 160

Goniaulax spinifera (Claparède and Lachmann) Diesing, 1866

Diesing, 1866, p. 96; Schiller, 1937, p. 297, fig. 305a-n; Wood, 1954, p. 263, fig. 174; *Peridinium spiniferum* Claparède and Lachmann, 1858-1861, p. 405.

Body rotund; epitheca subconical, tapering into a short apical horn; hypotheca with convex sides, with or without two small spines; girdle depressed, margins ridged, displaced two to three widths, overlapping; sulcus narrow, flaring at base. Length 35-45 μ.

Interoceanic, neritic or estuarine. Bahama Banks; Santaren Channel, West Channel, Straits of Florida; Brazil (north coast).

Fig. 161

Goniaulax turbynei Murray and Whitting, 1899

Murray and Whitting, 1899, p. 323, pl. 28 (fig. 4); Schiller, 1937, p. 299, fig. 307a-b.

Theca small, oval; epitheca subrotund with tapering apex and slight, tapering apical horn; girdle depressed, displaced about two widths; hypotheca rotund; sulcus depressed, widened and rounded near base; plates sculptured; sutures marked. Length about 40 μ.

Tropical Atlantic and Pacific oceans. Straits of Florida; Caribbean Sea.

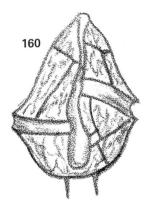

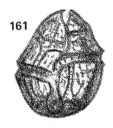

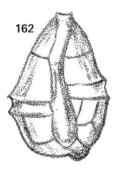

Fig. 162

Goniaulax unicornis, Lebour, 1925

Lebour, 1925, p. 92, pl. 13 (fig. 2a-b); Schiller, 1937, p. 303, fig. 314a-b.

Body ovate; epitheca higher than hypotheca, subconical, tapering into a very small apical horn; hypotheca low, rounded, with blunt process, asymmetrical at base; girdle depressed, with ridges, slightly displaced; sulcus not reaching base, ovate; plate formula 3', Oa, 6", 6''', 1p, 1''''. Length 30-35 μ. In the apical plate and lack of displacement this species resembles *Peridinium.*

Plymouth Sound. Sargasso Sea (Hulburt, 1962); Caribbean Sea.

163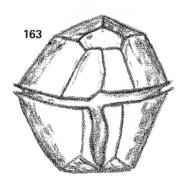

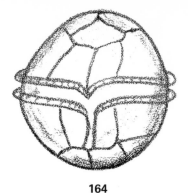

164

Genus GONIODOMA Stein

Cell polygonal or rounded; girdle equatorial, not displaced, with strong lists supported by spines; apical pore present but no apical or antapical horns; plate formula 3 or 4', 7", 5''', 3''''.

Fig. 163

Goniodoma polyedricum (Pouchet) Jörgensen, 1899

Jörgensen, 1899, p. 33; Schiller, 1937, p. 438, fig. 479a-e; Wood, 1954, p. 313, fig. 241a-c; *Peridinium polyedricum* Pouchet, 1883, p. 42, pl. 20 (fig. 34).

Cell polyhedral, heptagonal; epitheca with three corners, hypotheca with two; apical pore elongate, directed to one side; transverse section nearly circular; girdle equatorial, left-handed, ribbed girdle lists; theca strongly pored; sutures well marked. Length 30-60 μ.

Cosmopolitan in tropical and subtropical waters. Bahama Banks; West Channel, Santaren Channel, Straits of Florida; Benguela Current; Bermuda and Sargasso Sea (Hulburt, 1962); Brazil (north coast); Caribbean Sea.

Fig. 164

Goniodoma sphaericum Murray and Whitting, 1899

Murray and Whitting, 1899, p. 325, pl. 27, fig. 3; Wood, 1954, p. 313.

Cell spherical; apical pore small; girdle offset, with strong lists; plate formula 3', 7", 5''', 3''''. Diameter 35-50 μ.

Mediterranean Sea; Indian, Pacific, and Atlantic oceans. Straits of Florida; Caribbean Sea.

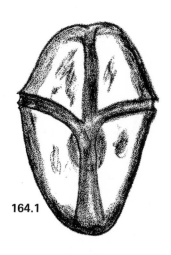

164.1

Genus GYMNODINIUM Stein

Body variable in shape, rotund to subconical; theca absent; girdle median, depressed but not displaced or only slightly so; sulcus may or may not extend onto epicone.

Fig. 164.1

Gymnodinium amphora Kofoid and Swezy, 1921

Kofoid and Swezy, 1921, p. 185, text fig. AA6, pl. 3 (fig. 26).

Body ovate; epicone subconical with rounded and slightly indented apex; hypocone larger than epicone, cordate; girdle anterior, depressed; sulcus extending from apex to base, flaring. Length 150 μ.

California coast. Caribbean Sea.

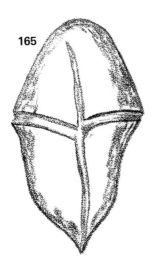

165

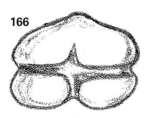

166

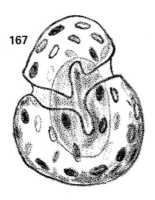

167

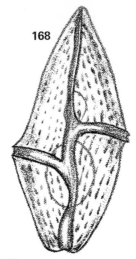

168

Fig. 166

Gymnodinium brevis Davis, 1948

Davis, 1948, p. 358.

Body small, obovate; epicone and hypocone low, rounded; apex with slight, rounded protuberance; girdle indented, straight; sulcus extending into epicone and reaching indented base. Length 20 μ. Very variable species.

Gulf of Mexico (Curl, 1959), where it caused mass mortality of fish.

Fig. 167

Gymnodinium cinctum Kofoid and Swezy, 1921

Kofoid and Swezy, 1921, p. 196, text fig. X28, pl. 7 (fig. 75); Wood, 1963*a*, p. 24, fig. 78.

Body roughly ovate; epicone subconical; hypocone rotund, larger than epicone; girdle anterior, displaced one width; sulcus rudimentary. Length 25 μ.

Oceanic; California coast; Coral Sea. Straits of Florida.

Fig. 168

Gymnodinium coeruleum Dogiel, 1906

Dogiel, 1906, pp. 34, 36, 40, 46, 47, fig. 2.

Body elongate, bioconical to 8-shaped, about twice as long as wide, flattened ventrally; girdle submedian, displaced about two widths; sulcus from apex to antapex, narrow on epicone, widening from girdle to antapex; base indented. Length 100 μ.

Coral Sea. Brazil (north coast).

Fig. 165

Gymnodinium auratum Kofoid and Swezy, 1921

Kofoid and Swezy, 1921, p. 187, text fig. Y13.

Body ovoid; epicone conical; girdle submedian, displaced more than one width; hypocone rounded; sulcus from apex to base, not indented. Length 60 μ.

La Jolla (California). Brazil (north coast).

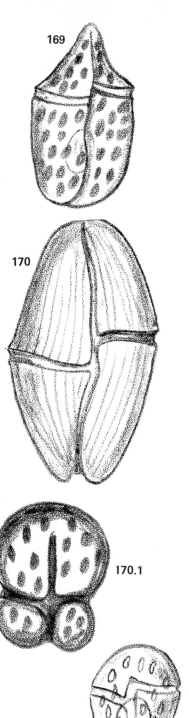

Fig. 169

Gymnodinium conicum Kofoid and Swezy, 1921

Kofoid and Swezy, 1921, p. 198, text fig. X27.

Body asymmetrical, depressed ventrally; epicone conical with blunt end, sides concave; hypocone much larger, base rounded, slightly depressed; girdle depressed, displaced, narrow; sulcus extending from apex to base, straight. Length 60-70 μ.

English Channel. Caribbean Sea; Brazil (north coast).

Fig. 170

Gymnodinium costatum Kofoid and Swezy, 1921

Kofoid and Swezy, 1921, p. 200, text fig. Z10, pl. 3 (fig. 33).

Body subovoid, large; girdle submedian, displaced; sulcus extends from apex to antapex; surface ridged. Length 150 μ.

Pacific Ocean. Brazil (north coast).

Fig. 170.1

Gymnodinium dissimile Kofoid and Swezy, 1921

Kofoid and Swezy, 1921, p. 204, text fig. X32, pl. 4 (fig. 35).

Epicone large, almost spherical; hypocone low, rounded, base indented; girdle deep, posterior; sulcus extending from about one-third distance from apex to indented base. Length 50 μ.

California coast. Caribbean Sea.

Fig. 171

Gymnodinium flavum Kofoid and Swezy, 1921

Kofoid and Swezy, 1921, p. 208, text fig. X7, pl. 9 (fig. 100); Wood, 1963*a*, p. 25, fig. 82.

Body minute, broadly elliptical, slightly compressed dorsoventrally; girdle submedian, displaced about twice its width; sulcus from girdle to base. Length 20-30 μ.

California coast; Coral Sea; Mediterranean Sea. Tropical Atlantic Ocean; Caribbean Sea; Straits of Florida; Brazil (north coast).

Fig. 172

Gymnodinium galaeforme Matzenauer, 1933

Matzenauer, 1933, p. 595; Wood, 1963*a*, p. 25, fig. 84.

Epicone helmet-shaped, sides slightly concave; girdle slightly displaced; hypocone with concave sides and antapex; sulcus reaching antapex. Length 60 μ.

Indian and Pacific oceans. Brazil (north coast); Caribbean Sea.

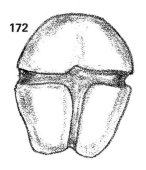

Fig. 173

Gymnodinium gelbum Kofoid, 1931

Kofoid, 1931, p. 13, pl. 1 (fig. 1); Schiller, 1933, p. 363, fig. 368; Wood, 1963*a*, p. 26, fig. 85.

Body rotund; epicone hemispherical; hypocone slightly depressed antapically; girdle median, displaced about one width; sulcus from girdle to antapex; chromatophores large, lanceolate. Length 40-50 μ.

Mutsu Bay (Japan); Solomon Islands. Benguela Current; Brazil (north coast); Caribbean Sea.

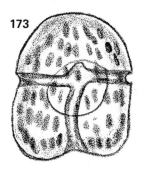

Fig. 174

Gymnodinium gibberum Schiller, 1928

Schiller, 1928, p. 149, fig. 26, pl. 5 (fig. 21); Schiller, 1933, p. 364, fig. 369.

Body elongate-oval; epicone and hypocone bluntly conical, slightly asymmetrical; epicone with longitudinal striations, hypocone with reticulate markings; girdle wide, somewhat deep; sulcus almost equal on epicone and hypocone. Length 40-50 μ.

Gulf of Naples. Caribbean Sea.

Fig. 175

Gymnodinium grammaticum (Pouchet) Kofoid and Swezy, 1921

Kofoid and Swezy, 1921, p. 217, text fig. X22.

Body small, rotund; girdle median, narrow; hypocone with strong posterior furrow; sulcus on hypocone only. Length 20-25 μ.

Mediterranean Sea; French coast; Coral Sea. Brazil (north coast); Caribbean Sea.

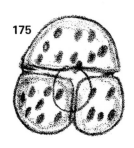

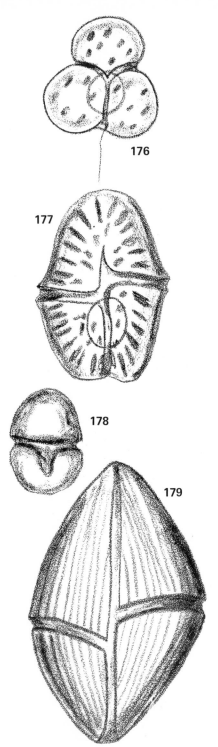

Fig. 176

Gymnodinium marinum Saville-Kent, 1880-1882

Saville-Kent, 1880-1882, p. 444, pl. 25 (figs. 60-61); Schiller, 1933, p. 382, fig. 391; Wood, 1963*a*, p. 26, fig. 88.

Body roughly ovate; epicone almost elliptical, narrower than hypocone, which is also rotund and deeply divided by narrow sulcus; girdle very narrow, constricting body. Length 30 μ.

English Channel; Coral Sea. Santaren Channel, Straits of Florida; Benguela Current; Brazil (north coast); Caribbean Sea.

Fig. 177

Gymnodinium mirabile Penard, 1891

Penard, 1891, pp. 11, 14, 16, 22, 25, 30, 56, pl. 5 (figs. 1-7); Schiller, 1933, p. 384, fig. 394.

Body somewhat angular; epicone domed, flaring at girdle; hypocone also flaring, base flat or slightly depressed; girdle slightly to greatly offset, strongly indented; sulcus extending about halfway on epicone and to base of hypocone. Length 80-90 μ. Very variable species, grading into *Gyrodinium*, several shapes in single cell cultures.

Bear Cut; Santaren Channel, Straits of Florida; Benguela Current; Brazil (north coast); Caribbean Sea.

Fig. 178

Gymnodinium mitratum Schiller, 1933

Schiller, 1933, p. 386, fig. 396a-c.

Body oval, not flattened; epicone rounded, slightly larger than hypocone which is also rounded; girdle depressed; sulcus not reaching base. Length 30-40 μ.

Attersee. Amazon estuary.

Fig. 179

Gymnodinium multistriatum Kofoid and Swezy, 1921

Kofoid and Swezy, 1921, p. 236, pl. 4 (fig. 37).

Body biconical to ovate; epicone slightly larger than hypocone; girdle approximately median, displaced at least one width; sulcus straight from apex to antapex, narrower than girdle. Length 100 μ.

Pacific Ocean. Brazil (north coast).

Fig. 180

Gymnodinium nanum Schiller, 1928

Schiller, 1928, p. 142, pl. 5 (fig. 17); Schiller, 1933, p. 389, fig. 401; Wood, 1963*a*, p. 27, fig. 91.

Body small; epicone hemispherical; hypocone ovate; girdle wide, displaced; sulcus short. Length 5 μ.

Adriatic and Coral seas. Straits of Florida.

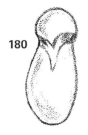

180

Fig. 181

Gymnodinium ochraceum Kofoid, 1931

Kofoid, 1931, p. 17, pl. 1 (fig. 6).

Cells broadly ovate; epicone subconical with rounded apex; hypocone rounded, base slightly indentate; girdle indented, slightly offset; sulcus on hypocone only, reaching base. Length 65 μ.

Mutsu Bay (Japan). Amazon region.

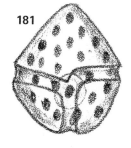

181

Fig. 182

Gymnodinium pachydermatum Kofoid and Swezy, 1921

Kofoid and Swezy, 1921, p. 239, text fig. AA5, pl. 3 (fig. 32).

Body broadly elliptical; epicone hemispherical; girdle submedian, displaced twice its width; sulcus on epicone, extending to base; hypocone slightly indented. Length 160 μ.

Pacific Ocean. Caribbean Sea.

182

Fig. 183

Gymnodinium punctatum Pouchet, 1887

Pouchet, 1887, p. 105, pl. 10 (fig. 7); Kofoid and Swezy, 1921, p. 244, text fig. BB18; Wood, 1963*a*, p. 27, fig. 94.

Body small, rotund; epicone hemispherical; hypocone deeply indented at antapex; girdle median; sulcus from girdle to antapex. Length 10 μ.

Off French coast; Coral Sea. Straits of Florida; Sargasso Sea; Gulf Stream (Hulburt, 1963); Bermuda (Hulburt, 1963); Venezuela (Hulburt, 1962); Brazil (north coast).

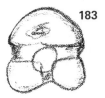

183

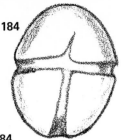

Fig. 184

Gymnodinium rotundatum Klebs, 1912

Klebs, 1912, pp. 392, 403, 439, fig. 5.

Body small, round, subspherical; girdle depressed, not displaced; sulcus from apex to antapex, narrow on epicone. Length 30-40 μ. Amazon delta; Caribbean Sea.

Fig. 185

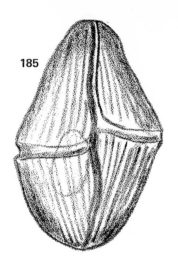

Gymnodinium rubrum Kofoid and Swezy, 1921

Kofoid and Swezy, 1921, p. 253, text figs. A, Y4, pl. 8 (fig. 86); Wood, 1963a, p. 28, fig. 97.

Body large, ovoid but labile in shape; girdle slightly posterior, wide, impressed, displaced; hypocone more asymmetrical than epicone and more irregular in outline; sulcus sinuous from apex to base, widening toward base; surface longitudinally striate. Length 100 μ.

California coast; Coral Sea. Straits of Florida.

Fig. 186

Gymnodinium scopulosum Kofoid and Swezy, 1921

Kofoid and Swezy, 1921, p. 244, pl. 1 (fig. 7).

Body ovate, tending to fusiform; girdle submedian, displaced about one-third width; sulcus from near apex to antapex. Length 50 μ.

Pacific Ocean. Brazil (north coast).

Fig. 187

Gymnodinium simplex (Lohmann) Kofoid and Swezy, 1921

Kofoid and Swezy, 1921, p. 256, text fig. BB8; Wood, 1963a, p. 28, fig. 99.

Form minute, ellipsoidal with wide median girdle; sulcus absent (Kofoid and Swezy), present in species seen and narrow in epicone (cf. Schiller, 1933, p. 413). Length 2-20 μ. Strains from different parts of the world differ markedly and diagnostic characters are few.

Cosmopolitan. Santaren Channel, West Channel, Straits of Florida; Benguela Current; Brazil (north coast); Caribbean Sea.

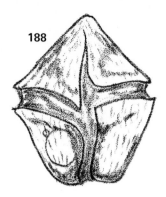

188

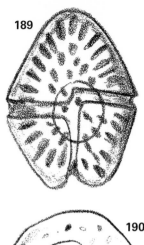

189

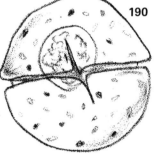

190

191

Fig. 188

Gymnodinium situla Kofoid and Swezy, 1921

Kofoid and Swezy, 1921, p. 257, text fig. Z6, pl. 1 (fig. 12); Wood, 1963*a,* p. 29, fig. 100.

Body of medium size, rotund; epicone bluntly conical; girdle slightly anterior, slightly displaced; sulcus from apex to base, narrow anteriorly. Length 60 μ.

California coast; Coral Sea. Straits of Florida.

Fig. 189

Gymnodinium splendens Lebour, 1925

Lebour, 1925, p. 34, pl. 5 (fig. 1); Schiller, 1933, p. 417, fig. 438; Wood, 1963*a,* p. 29, fig. 102.

Body ovate, flattened dorsoventrally; epicone and hypocone subequal, former subhemispherical, latter constricted at antapex; girdle offset about one width; sulcus from girdle to antapex, widened posteriorly. Length 50-60 μ.

English Channel; Coral Sea. Gulf of Mexico; Straits of Florida; Benguela Current.

Fig. 190

Gymnodinium variabile Herdman, 1924

Herdman, 1924, p. 80, figs. 35-45; Schiller, 1933, p. 424, fig. 446a-l.

Body rotund, variable in form; apex and antapex round or slightly flattened; girdle region may be flared, girdle narrow, depressed, slightly offset; sulcus small and narrow, slight on epicone. Length 8-40 μ. This species seems to vary similarly to *G. mirabile* as described by Kimball and Wood (1965).

In sand at Port Erin. Straits of Florida.

Genus GYRODINIUM Kofoid and Swezy

Theca absent; cell rounded or ovate; girdle strongly displaced; sulcus more or less longitudinal, usually extending on epicone, may reach base of hypocone.

Fig. 191

Gyrodinium calyptrographe Lebour, 1925

Lebour, 1925, p. 52, pl. 7 (fig. 3a-b).

Body angular, rotund; epicone subconical; apex rounded; hypocone subrotund; girdle deeply indented, offset three to four widths; sulcus deep and narrow, irregular. Length 30 μ.

Plymouth Sound. Caribbean Sea.

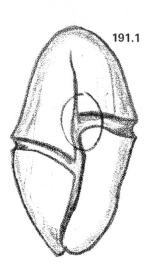

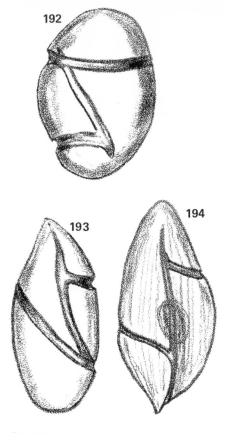

Fig. 191.1

Gyrodinium fissum (Levander) Kofoid and Swezy, 1921.

Kofoid and Swezy, 1921, p. 300, text fig. DD8, pl. 9 (fig. 95).

Body subovoidal; girdle displaced about three widths; sulcus from apex to antapex, slightly sigmoid. Length 45-60 μ.

Atlantic Ocean; Pacific Ocean. Brazil (north coast).

191.2

Gyrodinium glaebum Hulburt, 1957
Hulburt, 1957=*Gymnodinium mirabile*.

Epicone and hypocone equal, hemispherical; girdle wide and deep, displaced two to three times its width; sulcus extending onto epicone, sigmoid, wider on hypocone, extending to base forming a depression there. Length 100 μ.

Senix Creek (Hulburt, 1963).

Fig. 192

Gyrodinium grave (Meunier) Kofoid and Swezy, 1921

Kofoid and Swezy, 1921, p. 309.

Body ellipsoidal; girdle a descending left spiral, slightly constricting; sulcus from anterior end of girdle to near antapex. Length 60 μ.

Arctic Ocean. Brazil (north coast).

Fig. 193

Gyrodinium herbaceum Kofoid and Swezy, 1921

Kofoid and Swezy, 1921, p. 310, text fig. DD6.

Body subovoidal; girdle left spiral; widely displaced sulcus short above and below girdle with half a turn. Length 40 μ.

La Jolla (California). Brazil (north coast).

Fig. 194

Gyrodinium nasutum (Wulff) Schiller, 1933

Schiller, 1933, p. 481, fig. 512; Wood, 1963a, p. 32, fig. 110; *Spirodinium nasutum* Wulff, 1916, p. 108, pl. 1 (fig. 6a-c).

Body variable in shape, rather elongate-oval; at base is a small, blunt protuberance; girdle a spiral of one turn; sulcus in depressed ventral area, narrow, from near apex to base. Length 100 μ.

Barents Sea; Coral Sea. Caribbean Sea; Brazil (north coast).

195

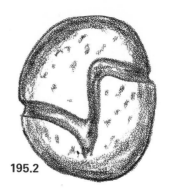

195.2

195.1

196

Fig. 195

Gyrodinium ochraceum Kofoid and Swezy, 1921

Kofoid and Swezy, 1921, p. 321, text fig. DD17, pl. 7 (figs. 76, 82).

Body bullet-shaped, acute at apex, rounded at antapex; girdle strongly displaced; sulcus slightly spiral. Length 110 μ.

California coast; Adriatic Sea; Coral Sea; Vitiaz Strait. Amazon region.

Fig. 195.1

Gyrodinium ovatum (Gourret) Kofoid and Swezy, 1921

Kofoid and Swezy, 1921, p. 322, text fig. EE7; *Gymnodinium ovatum* Gourret, p. 88, pl. 1 (fig. 22).

Body fusiform with rounded ends, apex more acute than antapex; epicone larger than hypocone; girdle posterior, ending near base; sulcus reaching from girdle to base. Length 70 μ.

Mediterranean Sea. Caribbean Sea.

Fig. 195.2

Gyrodinium ovoideum Kofoid and Swezy, 1921

Kofoid and Swezy, 1921, p. 323, text figs. F, CC, pl. 9 (fig. 106).

Body round; epicone and hypocone hemispherical, subequal; girdle depressed, widely displaced; sulcus not on epicone, sigmoid, not reaching base. Length 45-75 μ.

Pacific Ocean. Caribbean Sea.

Fig. 196

Gyrodinium pingue (Schütt) Kofoid and Swezy, 1921

Kofoid and Swezy, 1921, p. 327, text fig. DD15, pl. 4 (fig. 38); Wood, 1963*a*, p. 32, fig. 112; *Gymnodinium spiralis* var. *pingue* Schütt, 1895, pl. 21 (fig. 65).

Body elongate-oval to fusiform, broadly rounded posteriorly, narrowly so anteriorly; girdle a descending left spiral displaced about one transdiameter; sulcus from near apex to near antapex, slightly sinuous. Length 55 u.

Atlantic Ocean; Mediterranean Sea. California coast; Barents Sea; Coral Sea. Caribbean Sea.

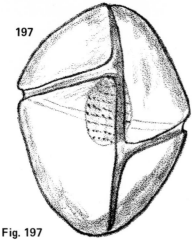

Fig. 197

Gyrodinium prunus (Wulff) Lebour, 1925

Lebour, 1925, p. 52, fig. 14a; Wood, 1963*a*, p. 33, fig. 113.

Body plum-shaped; girdle narrow, forming one turn; sulcus slightly curved. Length 40-45 μ.

Barents and Coral seas. Straits of Florida; Brazil (north coast).

Fig. 198

Gyrodinium spirale (Bergh) Kofoid and Swezy, 1921

Kofoid and Swezy, 1921, p. 332, pl. 4 (fig. 43); Wood, 1963*a*, p. 33, fig. 114; *Gymnodinium spirale* Bergh, 1881, p. 66.

Body fusiform, blunter at apex; girdle steeply inclined spiral; sulcus from apex to antapex; surface striate. Length 100-200 μ.

California coast; Coral Sea. Straits of Florida.

Fig. 199

Gyrodinium virgatum Kofoid and Swezy, 1921

Kofoid and Swezy, 1921, p. 339, text fig. DD21, pl. 10 (fig. 112); Schiller, 1933, p. 505, fig. 536.

Body asymmetrically rhomboidal; epicone conical, sides slightly rounded; hypocone truncate conical, base flat; girdle indented with slight lists, displaced more than one-third cell length; sulcus straight, reaching from apex to base; surface of cell striate. Length 80-100 μ.

Pacific Ocean off California. Straits of Florida.

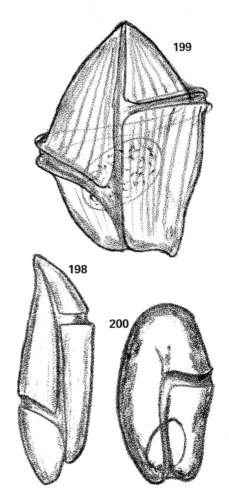

Genus HEMIDINIUM Stein

Body asymmetrically elliptical, more or less constricted dorsoventrally; girdle incomplete, forming a left spiral; sulcus well developed; theca with seventeen thin plates.

Fig. 200

Hemidinium nasutum Stein, 1883

Stein, 1883, p. 91, pl. 2 (figs. 23-26); Schiller, 1937, p. 89, fig. 75a-h; Wood, 1954, p. 222, fig. 85.

Body asymmetrically oval; girdle median, a descending left spiral of half a turn; sulcus confined to hypocone, reaching posterior margin. Length 25-50 μ.

Fresh to salt water, estuarine. West Channel, Straits of Florida.

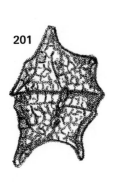

201

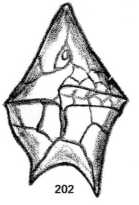

202

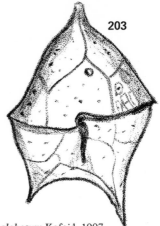

203

Genus HETERODINIUM Kofoid

Body more or less asymmetrical, strongly flattened dorsoventrally, often flexed, usually with two unequal antapical spines; apical pore may be on a tapering horn or epitheca may be rounded; pore present on ventral surface of theca; girdle partly developed, without lists, posterior edge of girdle hardly discernible; theca reticulate or porulate.

Fig. 201

Heterodinium angulatum Kofoid and Michener, 1911

Kofoid and Michener, 1911, p. 284; Kofoid and Adamson, 1933, p. 51, pl. 6 (figs. 1-2).

Body more or less quadrilateral; epitheca almost rectangular, broader than long, tapering into short apical horn and expanding to girdle, sides biconvex; hypotheca almost rectangular with tapering convex sides extending into two even and parallel antapical horns; plate sutures very marked; surface of plates strongly reticulate. Length 80-100 μ.

Eastern tropical Pacific Ocean. Santaren Channel, Straits of Florida; Brazil (north coast); Caribbean Sea.

Fig. 202

Heterodinium dispar Kofoid and Adamson, 1933

Kofoid and Adamson, 1933, p. 59, pl. 5 (figs. 2-3), pl. 15 (fig. 20).

Epitheca conical; girdle left-handed, wide overhang of anterior girdle list; sulcus not reaching antapex, narrow; antapical horns very unequal, right small, pointed, directed at about 45° to longitudinal axis. Length 70-80 μ.

Tropical Pacific Ocean. Caribbean area.

Fig. 203

Heterodinium globosum Kofoid, 1907

Kofoid, 1907b, p. 181, pl. 8 (fig. 51); Kofoid and Adamson, 1933, p. 45, pl. 4 (figs. 1-4), pl. 15 (fig. 10).

Body globose; apical horn small, tapering; antapicals stout, unequal; base asymmetrical; surface incompletely and irregularly reticulate. Length 100-120 μ.

Tropical waters; eastern Pacific Ocean. Caribbean Sea.

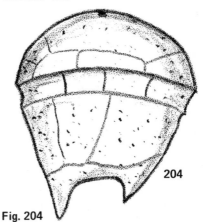

204

Fig. 204

Heterodinium inaequale (Kofoid) Schiller, 1937

Schiller, 1937, p. 344, pl. 372a-c; *H. laticinctum* Kofoid, 1906, p. 354, pl. 7 (fig. 46).

A large species with a broad and very oblique girdle; epitheca semicircular; hypotheca deep, trapezoidal, with rather small incurved antapical horns which are subequal; surface smooth, porulate. Length 80-105 μ.

Tropical interoceanic species. Caribbean Sea; Brazil (north coast).

73

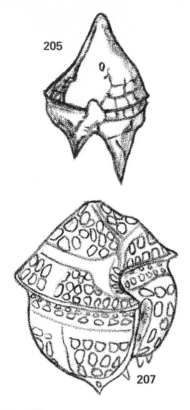

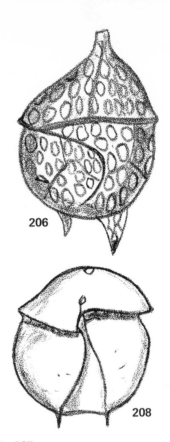

Fig. 205

Heterodinium leiorhynchum (Murray and Whitting) Kofoid, 1906

Kofoid, 1906, p. 358; Kofoid and Adamson, 1933, p. 64, pl. 15 (fig. 22); *Peridinium leiorhynchum* Murray and Whitting, 1899, p. 326, pl. 29 (fig. 2).

Epitheca conical in ventral view, conical with apical horn in lateral view; hypotheca rounded with two slightly unequal, pointed antapicals directed rearward. Length 100 μ.

Tropical waters of Atlantic Ocean. Pacific Ocean; Mediterranean Sea.

Fig. 206

Heterodinium mediterraneum Pavillard, 1932

Pavillard, 1932, p. 3, fig. 3.

Body rotund with conical epitheca and apical horn; hypotheca suborbicular with one small and one large, rugose antapical spine; girdle displaced about two widths. Length 40-60 μ.

Mediterranean Sea; Pacific Ocean. Brazil (north coast); Caribbean Sea.

Fig. 207

Heterodinium milneri (Murray and Whitting) Kofoid, 1906

Kofoid, 1906, p. 353; *Peridinium milneri* Murray and Whitting, 1899, p. 327, pl. 29 (fig. 3a-b).

Body subspheroidal with conical epitheca and a short apical horn; hypotheca rotund with four finned antapical spines; girdle displaced. Length 60 μ.

Coral Sea. Tropical Atlantic Ocean.

Fig. 208

Heterodinium minutum Kofoid and Michener, 1911

Kofoid and Michener, 1911, p. 285; Kofoid and Adamson, 1933, p. 34, figs. 4-7, pl. 15 (fig. 5).

Body rotund; epitheca rounded, low; anterior girdle list overhanging; hypotheca rotund, much deeper than epitheca; body smooth; sulcus widening to base; two small, even basal spines. Length 40 μ.

Pacific Ocean. Western Caribbean Sea.

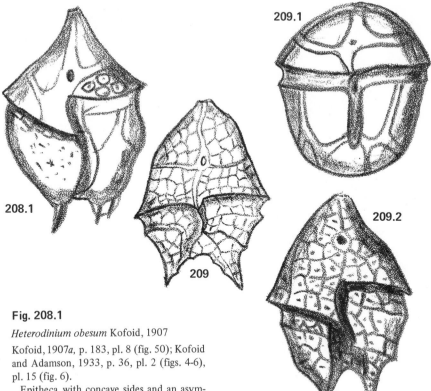

209.1

208.1

209

209.2

Fig. 208.1

Heterodinium obesum Kofoid, 1907

Kofoid, 1907*a*, p. 183, pl. 8 (fig. 50); Kofoid and Adamson, 1933, p. 36, pl. 2 (figs. 4-6), pl. 15 (fig. 6).

Epitheca with concave sides and an asymmetrical apical horn; hypotheca irregularly rounded with three antapicals with spines, set at an angle to the longitudinal axis; girdle with large overhang, displaced; sulcus deep, sigmoid, widening to base. Length 50-60 μ.

Eastern tropical Pacific Ocean. Caribbean Sea.

Fig. 209

Heterodinium scrippsi Kofoid, 1906

Kofoid, 1906, p. 342, pl. 17 (figs. 1-5a-b); Kofoid and Adamson, 1933, p. 81, pl. 5 (fig. 1), pl. 15 (fig. 18), pl. 18 (figs. 48-51).

Body angular; epitheca much larger than hypotheca, truncate-conical with slightly protruding apical horn; hypotheca low, subconical, with slightly concave right and convex left margins; antapical horns short, stout, conical, and pointed; post-margin asymmetrically concave; surface coarsely reticulate, areolae quadrilateral to polygonal, smallest at girdle; overhang wide. Length 150 μ.

Pacific and Atlantic oceans; Mediterranean Sea. Caribbean Sea; Brazil (north coast).

Fig. 209.1

Heterodinium sphaerodeum Kofoid, 1906

Kofoid, 1906, p. 351, pl. 3 (fig. 15).

Body almost spherical; epitheca rounded, low; girdle even, depressed, anterior; sulcus not reaching antapex; hypotheca rounded; surface reticulate. Length 40-50 μ.

California region. Caribbean Sea.

Fig. 209.2

Heterodinium superbum Kofoid, 1907

Kofoid, 1907*a*, p. 185, pl. 8 (fig. 49); Kofoid and Adamson, 1933, p. 3, pl. 4 (figs. 5-6), pl. 15 (fig. 9).

Epitheca conical, tapering to low apical horn; hypotheca angular with two uneven antapicals; girdle deep with large overhang; sulcus deep and wide; surface reticulate with pores. Length 130 μ.

Eastern tropical Pacific Ocean, rare. Caribbean Sea.

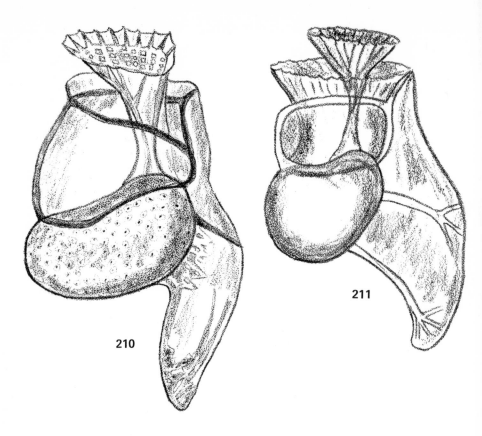

210

211

Genus HISTIONEIS Stein

Body usually wider than long, rounded to kidney-shaped; epitheca low; girdle wider dorsally; lists large, closed, anterior girdle list usually cylindrical with flared and ribbed forward part; posterior list cylindrical to gibbous with one dorsal and one ventral rib and submarginal cross-rib and pouches on each side; left sulcal list usually large, diverse in shape, often tongue-shaped and may be bizarrely patterned.

Fig. 210

Histioneis carinata Kofoid, 1907

Kofoid, 1907*a,* p. 203, pl. 16 (fig. 98); Kofoid and Skogsberg, 1928, p. 663, fig. 95 (1), pl. 21 (figs. 1, 8).

Body boat-shaped, higher ventrally; anterior girdle list funnel-shaped, strongly ribbed; posterior list gibbous, narrowing near apex, then dorsally flared, hyaline; body porulate; left sulcal list narrow to R_2, then widening and curved; R_3 posteroventral, terminating sulcal list which is rugosely thickened, especially in the after part. Length 90 μ.

Tropical Pacific and Atlantic oceans. Straits of Florida.

Fig. 211

Histioneis cerasus Bohm, 1931

Bohm, 1931, in Schiller, 1933, p. 229, fig. 221; Wood, 1963*a,* p. 14, fig. 43.

Body subrotund; epitheca flattened; anterior girdle list tubular, then flared, ribbed in flared portion; posterior list slightly gibbous and hyaline, then slightly flared, ribbed; sulcal list well developed, widest at R_3 which is ventral; R_2 and R_3 almost parallel and branched. Length 150 μ.

Pacific and Atlantic oceans. Straits of Florida.

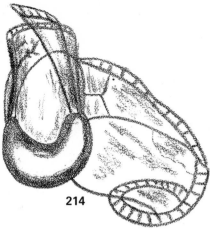

212

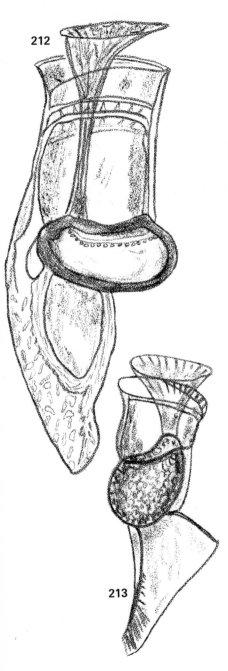

213

Fig. 212

Histioneis depressa Schiller, 1928

Schiller, 1928, p. 84, fig. 43; Schiller, 1933, p. 237, fig. 230.

Body kidney-shaped; epitheca depressed;

214

anterior girdle list tubular, then flared, rugose; posterior list tubular with slightly flared end; sulcal list extending strongly posteriorly with window between posterior R_2 and R_3 which anastomose. Length 60-70 μ.

Adriatic Sea. Straits of Florida.

Fig. 213

Histioneis elongata Kofoid and Michener, 1911

Kofoid and Michener, 1911, p. 295; Wood, 1963*a*, p. 16, fig. 47a.

Body ovate; anterior girdle list of moderate height, funnel-shaped, striate; posterior girdle list moderate, hyaline; left sulcal list cuneate, R_3 long, with cross-rib extending ventrally; sail triangular, extended posteriorly from R_2 to R_3. Length 120 μ.

Pacific Ocean. Brazil (north coast); Caribbean Sea.

Fig. 214

Histioneis helenae Murray and Whitting, 1899

Murray and Whitting, 1899, p. 333, pl. 33 (fig. 2); Wood, 1963*a*, p. 16, fig. 48.

Body in side view reniform; anterior girdle list long, tubular and curved, with striate, funnel-shaped opening; posterior list long, cylindrical, reticulate; epitheca saddle-shaped; two hyaline lobes on each side of posterior list; left sulcal list extending into sail from R_3 and undulate; R_3 submarginal; sail with submarginal thickening. Length 140-160 μ.

Atlantic and Pacific oceans. Brazil (north coast).

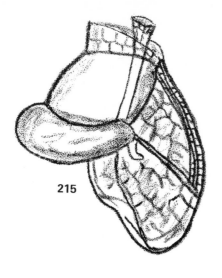

215

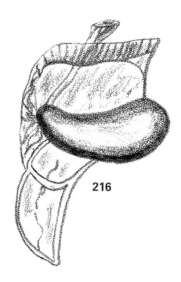

216

217

Fig. 216

Histioneis hyalina Kofoid and Michener, 1911

Kofoid and Michener, 1911, p. 296; Wood, 1963*a*, p. 17, fig. 50.

Body boat-shaped in lateral outline, slightly higher dorsally; anterior girdle list with long, narrow tube and slight funnel; posterior girdle list slightly gibbous dorsally, hyaline; left sulcal list narrow, R_2 directed posteriorly, joined to R_3 near middle, R_3 slightly ventral posteriorly. Length 50-60 μ.

Tropical Indian and Pacific oceans. Benguela Current; Brazil (north coast); Caribbean Sea.

Fig. 215

Histioneis hippoperoides Kofoid and Michener, 1911

Kofoid and Michener, 1911, p. 296; Kofoid and Skogsberg, 1928, p. 701, fig. 96 (5), pl. 23 (figs. 1, 3).

Body reniform, higher dorsally than ventrally; anterior girdle list cylindrical with flaring ribbed end; posterior list gibbous, reticulate above submarginal rib; left sulcal list large, rounded, ventral with wide frills, R_2 straight, directed posteriorly at about 30°, R_3 arising midway between R_2 and antapex; surface reticulate. Length 100 μ.

Pacific Ocean. Caribbean Sea.

Fig. 217

Histioneis inclinata Kofoid and Skogsberg, 1928

Kofoid and Skogsberg, 1928, p. 652, pl. 95 (fig. 13).

Body subrotund; epitheca low; anterior girdle list flared, longer dorsally than ventrally; posterior list slightly gibbous and flared at end; left sulcal list short, ending on ventral surface; margin rounded, surface reticulate; R_3 absent. Length 20-30 μ.

Pacific Ocean. Brazil (north coast).

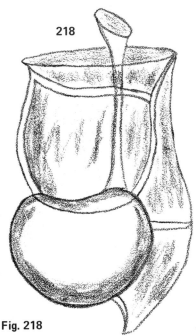

218

219

220

Fig. 218

Histioneis inornata Kofoid and Michener, 1911

Kofoid and Michener, 1911, p. 297; Kofoid and Skogsberg, 1928, p. 654, fig. 85.

Body rounded, depressed above; anterior girdle list funnel-shaped, flared; posterior list gibbous, wider than body; sulcal list of even width, rounded toward base but not reaching base; R_2 short, directed backward. Length 35-40 μ.

Tropical Pacific and Atlantic oceans. Straits of Florida.

Fig. 219

Histioneis jorgenseni Schiller, 1928

Schiller, 1928, p. 83, fig. 42; Schiller, 1933, p. 226, fig. 217.

Body subrotund; epitheca flattened; anterior girdle list cylindrical with flared end, may be ribbed; posterior list somewhat gibbous, hyaline; sulcal list ventral, extending well posteriorly; R_2 bending posteriorly, anastomosing with R_3 about halfway. Length 80 μ.

Mediterranean Sea. Straits of Florida.

Fig. 220

Histioneis longicollis Kofoid, 1907

Kofoid, 1907*b*, p. 204, pl. 16, fig. 100; Wood, 1963*a*, p. 18, fig. 54.

Body obliquely rotund; anterior girdle lists with long tube and striate funnel; girdle moderately raised; posterior girdle list cylindrical, reticulate; left sulcal list narrow, margin gently sigmoid; R_2 directed posteriorly to unite or nearly unite with R_3, which is ventral, posterior, and distally branched. Length 70-80 μ.

Eastern tropical Pacific Ocean; Coral Sea. Straits of Florida; Brazil (north coast); Caribbean Sea.

79

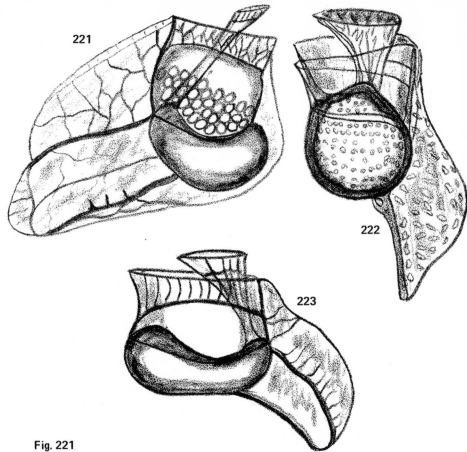

Fig. 221

Histioneis milneri Murray and Whitting, 1899.

Murray and Whitting, 1899, p. 33, pl. 33 (fig. 2).

Body sausage-shaped to rounded; girdle anterior; anterior girdle list with moderate tube and angled flare, ribbed; posterior list slightly gibbous, anteriorly reticulate; R_2 and R_3 long, parallel, R_3 sigmoid; sail broad, ventral; anterior and outer parts reticulate. Length 120 μ.

Indian Ocean. Brazil (north coast).

Fig. 222

Histioneis oxypteris Schiller, 1928

Schiller, 1928, p. 84, pl. 3 (fig. 6); Schiller, 1933, p. 225, fig. 215.

Body rotund; epitheca raised; anterior girdle list funnel-shaped, flared from epitheca, short, irregularly ribbed; posterior list hyaline, cylindrical, not gibbous; sulcal list almost rhomboidal, terminating at a long R_3 which is slightly ventral; list thickened. Length 40 μ.

Mediterranean Sea. Straits of Florida.

Fig. 223

Histioneis panaria Kofoid and Skogsberg, 1928

Kofoid and Skogsberg, 1928, p. 659, pl. 85 (figs. 8-9).

Body sausage-shaped; girdle anterior; epitheca small; anterior girdle list short, flared, ribbed; posterior list larger than body, irregular, upper part ribbed; left sulcal list triangular; R_2 straight, inclined dorsally, more or less parallel to R_3, which terminates sail; lists may be reticulate. Length 60-70 μ.

Indian Ocean. Brazil (north coast).

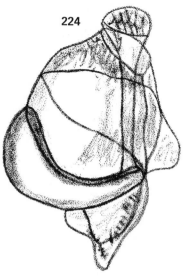

224

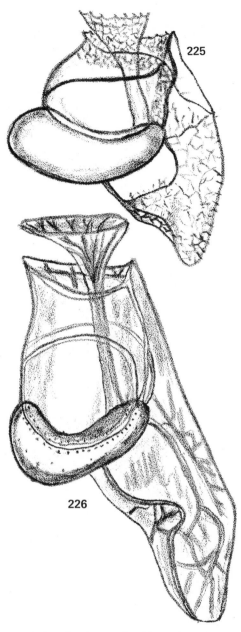

225

226

Fig. 224

Histioneis panda Kofoid and Michener, 1911

Kofoid and Michener, 1911, p. 298; Wood, 1963*b*, p. 7, fig. 18.

Body sausage-shaped, higher dorsally; girdle anterior; anterior girdle list with long tube and symmetrical, reticulate funnel; posterior list strongly gibbous, contracted anteriorly, upper part reticulate; left sulcal list posterior with R_2 joining R_3; sail triangular and supported by extension of R_3. Length 80 μ.

Pacific Ocean; Indian Ocean. Straits of Florida.

Fig. 225

Histioneis pietschmanni Bohm, 1933

Bohm, in Schiller, 1933, p. 247, fig. 241; Wood, 1963*a*, p. 19, fig. 59.

Body reniform, higher dorsally; anterior girdle list cylindrical with reticulate funnel; posterior list gibbous, margins reticulate; left sulcal list with irregular margin, reticulate; R_2 branches, posterior part joining marginal R_3 to form a semicircle. Length 100 μ.

Indian Ocean; Coral Sea. Caribbean Sea.

Fig. 226

Histioneis pulchra Kofoid, 1907

Kofoid, 1907*a*, p. 205, pl. 16 (fig. 99); Kofoid and Skogsberg, 1928, p. 686, fig. 96, pl. 21 (figs. 4, 7), pl. 23 (fig. 2).

Body kidney-shaped; anterior girdle list tubular, flared at end, with anastomosing ribs; posterior list gibbous, high, with reticulate ribs; sulcal list prolonged into sail much longer than body; R_2 and R_3 convoluted and anastomosing with extensions supporting sail. Length 130-150 μ.

Southwest and eastern tropical Pacific Ocean. Straits of Florida.

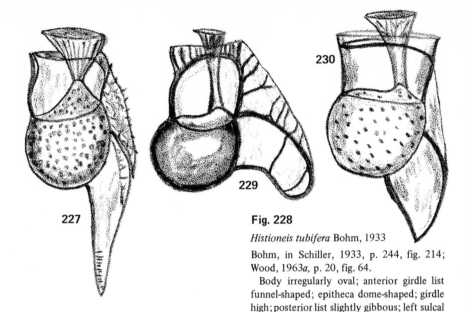

227

Fig. 228

228

Fig. 227

Histioneis remora Stein, 1883

Stein, 1883, p. 22, fig. 11; Wood, 1963b, p. 7, fig. 19.

Body subcircular; epitheca in lateral view bluntly conical; hypotheca rotund; anterior girdle list with short tube and long funnel, evenly ribbed; posterior list cylindrical, slightly gibbous, hyaline; left sulcal list long and narrow, tapering to an acute point; R_2 marginal to marginal R_3, both bent posteriorly; list partly reticulate. Length 130 μ.

Pacific Ocean; Arafura Sea; Mediterranean Sea.

Fig. 228

Histioneis tubifera Bohm, 1933

Bohm, in Schiller, 1933, p. 244, fig. 214; Wood, 1963a, p. 20, fig. 64.

Body irregularly oval; anterior girdle list funnel-shaped; epitheca dome-shaped; girdle high; posterior list slightly gibbous; left sulcal list with R_2 short, ventral, R_3 directed posteriorly, marginal, almost in vertical axis of cell, margin gently rounded. Length 50 μ.

Indian and Pacific oceans. Brazil (north coast).

Fig. 229

Histioneis variabilis Schiller, 1933

Schiller, 1933, p. 231, fig. 223a-d.

Body cherry-shaped, variable; anterior girdle list with long tube and striate funnel; girdle slightly concave; posterior girdle list somewhat gibbous, variable; R_2 and R_3 both ventral, forming one or two loops; left sulcal list reinforced in various patterns. Length 50-60 μ.

Adriatic Sea; Atlantic and Pacific oceans. Brazil (north coast); Caribbean Sea.

Fig. 230

Histioneis voucki Schiller, 1928

Schiller, 1928, p. 82, fig. 4; Schiller, 1933, p. 225, fig. 216; Wood, 1963a, p. 20, fig. 66.

Body rotund, slightly reniform; anterior girdle list funnel-shaped, ribbed; posterior list slightly flaring, hyaline; left sulcal list hyaline, margin sigmoid; R_2 and R_3 both ventral, forming the margins of the posterior part of the list and united acutely. Length 40-50 μ.

Adriatic Sea; north Tasman and south Coral seas. Caribbean Sea; Brazil (north coast).

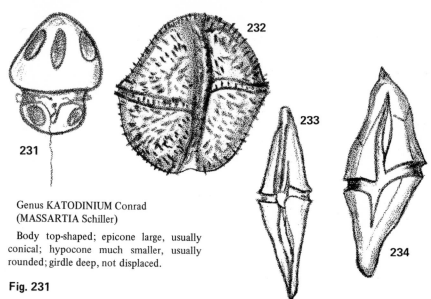

232

233

234

Genus KATODINIUM Conrad
(MASSARTIA Schiller)

Body top-shaped; epicone large, usually conical; hypocone much smaller, usually rounded; girdle deep, not displaced.

Fig. 231

Katodinium rotundatum (Lohmann) Conrad, 1927

Amphidinium rotundatum Lohmann, 1908, pp. 147, 261, 324, pl. 17, fig. 9.

Body top-shaped; epicone conical, sides straight to convex; hypocone small, hemispherical, very low; girdle posterior, wide, depressed; sulcus absent. Length 12-15 μ.

Straits of Florida; Bear Cut; Venezuela; Sargasso Sea; Gulf Stream; Bermuda (Hulburt); Brazil (north coast); Caribbean Sea.

Genus MELANODINIUM Schiller

Body ovate to subspherical; girdle median, slightly offset; sulcus extending from apex to antapex in deep furrow; surface with three- to four-sided areoles with triangular hyaline platelets arising from sides; plates masked by areoles.

Fig. 232

Melanodinium nigricans Schiller, 1937

Schiller, 1937, p. 320, fig. 336a-d.

Body ovate, almost circular; epitheca and hypotheca roughly hemispherical, with deep groove from apex to base containing sulcus; plates not obvious, masked by dense, three- to four-sided areoles with central pore and three-sided platelets protruding from sides of areoles. Length 50-70 μ.

Red Sea; Solomon Islands. Brazil (north coast).

Genus MURRAYELLA Kofoid

Body fusiform to subspherical; no apical pore; epitheca and hypotheca subequal; girdle depressed, slightly displaced; sulcus narrow; surface porulate.

Fig. 233

Murrayella biconica (Murray and Whitting) Pavillard, 1931

Pavillard, 1931, p. 98, pl. 3 (fig. 15).

Body biconical, ends acute; epitheca and hypotheca subequal; girdle submedian, slightly displaced; sulcus narrow; surface porulate. Length 150 μ.

East Coral Sea. Warm Atlantic waters; West Channel, Straits of Florida; Benguela Current; Brazil (north coast); Caribbean Sea.

Fig. 234

Murrayella intermedia Pavillard, 1916

Pavillard, 1916, p. 44, pl. 2 (fig. 5); Schiller, 1937, p. 450, fig. 495.

Theca biconical, sides undulate, slightly flared at girdle; apex rounded, antapex with marked spine; girdle offset about half its width, recessed, lists present; sulcus extending about halfway on epitheca, slightly twisted on hypotheca, winged. Length 100-120 μ.

Tropical Atlantic and Pacific oceans. Brazil (north coast); Caribbean Sea.

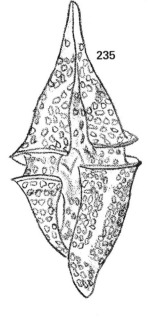

Fig. 235

Murrayella spinosa Kofoid, 1907

Kofoid, 1907*b*, p. 192, pl. 9 (fig. 57); Wood, 1963*a*, p. 43, fig. 158.

Theca biconical; epitheca higher than hypotheca, sides slightly convex to slightly concave; girdle deeply recessed, coarsely porulate; sulcus narrowing toward apex, twisted on hypotheca, winged; theca coarsely areolate. Length 45-50 μ.

Tropical Pacific Ocean. Straits of Florida.

Genus NEMATODINIUM Kofoid and Swezy

Cell fusiform; nematocysts present; girdle with more than one turn, displaced more than one and one-half transdiameters; sulcus also twisted with a posterior turn on dorsal side of antapex; ocellus posterior.

Fig. 236

Nematodinium torpedo Kofoid and Swezy, 1921

Kofoid and Swezy, 1921, p. 426, pl. 11 (fig. 124); Wood, 1963*a*, p. 35, fig. 123.

Body fusiform, long; girdle a left-hand spiral of over two turns; sulcus spiral. Length 80-100 μ.

California coast; Coral Sea. Straits of Florida; Brazil (north coast); Caribbean Sea.

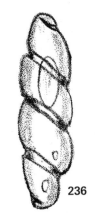

Genus NOCTILUCA Suriray

Body very large, almost macroscopic, inflated, reniform to sphaeroidal, largely vacuolate; sulcus very deep, forming an apical trough; longitudinal flagellum short, transverse flagellum reduced to a projecting mobile tooth; large tentacle at posterior end of sulcus; spores multiple, gymnodinioid.

Fig. 237

Noctiluca miliaris Suriray (MSS. Lamarck) 1816

Body inflated, somewhat reniform; no distinction between epicone and hypocone; sulcus very deep, mouth region extended anteriorly as an apical trough; longitudinal flagellum short, transverse flagellum as a mobile tooth; tentacle at posterior end of sulcus; zoospores gymnodinioid. Diameter 1,000 μ.

Cosmopolitan in warm water, neritic. Straits of Florida; off French Guiana.

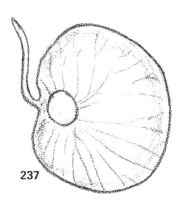

Genus ORNITHOCERCUS Stein

Body subcircular to subovate, compressed laterally; epitheca low and disk-like; girdle usually wide, oblique; girdle lists large and funnel-shaped, extending forward of body, usually ribbed or reticulate; left sulcal list large and sail-like, often extending dorsally of antapex, often ribbed or reticulate.

Fig. 238

Ornithocercus carolinae Kofoid, 1907

Kofoid, 1907a, p. 205, pl. 15 (fig. 92); Kofoid and Skogsberg, 1928, p. 572, fig. 89, pl. 17 (figs. 1, 6).

Body rotund; epitheca higher ventrally; anterior girdle list widely flared, strongly ribbed; posterior list slightly flared, strongly ribbed; sulcal list trilobed, strongly sculptured, with numerous ancillary ribs and marginal rib. Length 40-50 μ.

Widely spread but rare in tropical and subtropical waters. Straits of Florida.

Fig. 239

Ornithocercus formosus Kofoid and Michener, 1911

Kofoid and Michener, 1911, p. 300; Kofoid and Skogsberg, 1928, p. 577, fig. 91, pl. 17 (figs. 4-5).

Body ovate; anterior girdle list flared, ribbed; posterior list somewhat flared, strongly ribbed; left sulcal list extending to dorsal area, supported by strong rib, lobed between this and R_3, list strongly thickened with series of incomplete ribs, whole list roughly quadrilateral. Length 60 μ.

Tropical Pacific Ocean. Straits of Florida.

Fig. 240

Ornithocercus heteroporus Kofoid, 1907

Kofoid, 1907a, p. 206, pl. 12 (fig. 70); Kofoid and Skogsberg, 1928, p. 517, figs. 75-76, pl. 18 (figs. 1, 3).

Body subcircular; anterior girdle list flared, strongly ribbed; posterior girdle list somewhat flared with straight ribs; sulcal list widening to R_3, ending slightly ventrally with concave margin supported by marginal rib and several (two to four) supplementary ribs. Length 30-40 μ.

Tropical and subtropical waters. Straits of Florida.

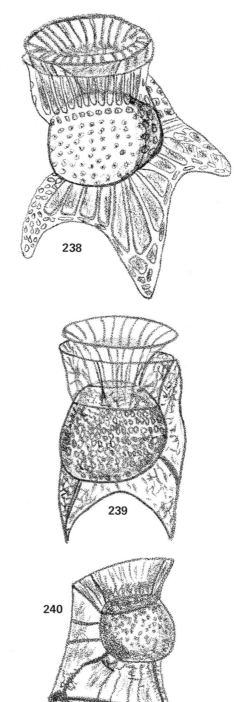

238

239

240

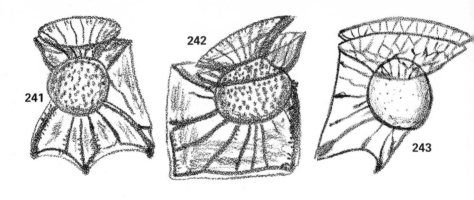

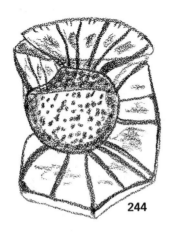

244

Fig. 241

Ornithocercus magnificus Stein, 1883

Stein, 1883, 1895 partim., pl. 23 (figs. 1-2); Schiller, 1933, p. 198, fig. 190a-b.

Body subcircular; girdle lists large, funnel-shaped, ribbed; left sulcal list ends on dorsal side of body with two posterior lobes, center lobe supported typically by three ribs forming a diamond. Length 40-120 μ.

Cosmopolitan in warmer water. West Channel, Straits of Florida; Benguela Current; Brazil (north coast); Caribbean Sea.

Fig. 242

Ornithocercus quadratus Schütt, 1900

Schütt, 1900, pls. 5, 6, figs. 1-4, 12, 13; Schiller, 1933, p. 204, fig. 193.

Body rotund; girdle wider on dorsal side; anterior and posterior girdle lists funnel-shaped with numerous ribs; left sulcal list quadrate, finishing parallel with dorsal plane, usually with a submarginal rib. Length 50-75 μ.

Tropical and subtropical species in all oceans. Straits of Florida; Benguela Current.

Fig. 243

Ornithocercus splendidus Schütt, 1893

Schütt, 1893, p. 272, fig. 82; Kofoid and Skogsberg, 1928, p. 521, figs. 77, 85, pl. 16 (figs. 2, 4), pl. 17 (fig. 3).

Body ovate, small; anterior and posterior girdle lists flared, about twice diameter of body, reticulately ribbed; sulcal list bilobed, ventral with strongly reinforced main ribs and ancillary ribs, often short. Length 50-100 μ.

Widely distributed but rarely numerous in tropical and subtropical waters. Western Caribbean Sea.

Fig. 244

Ornithocercus steini Schütt, 1900

Schütt, 1900; Wood, 1954, p. 209, fig. 62.

Body subrotund; girdle wider dorsally than ventrally; anterior girdle list supported by strong ribs, funnel-shaped; posterior list also ribbed; left sulcal list wide, margin rounded, almost parallel with body, ending dorsally; ribs more or less evenly spaced, last rib reaching margin of ventral-side of wing. Length 50-70 μ.

Cosmopolitan in tropical and subtropical waters. Straits of Florida; Benguela Current; Caribbean Sea.

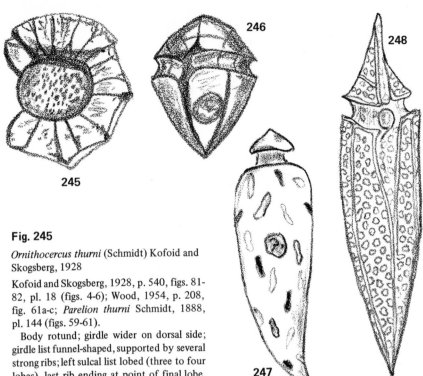

245

246

248

247

Fig. 245

Ornithocercus thurni (Schmidt) Kofoid and Skogsberg, 1928

Kofoid and Skogsberg, 1928, p. 540, figs. 81-82, pl. 18 (figs. 4-6); Wood, 1954, p. 208, fig. 61a-c; *Parelion thurni* Schmidt, 1888, pl. 144 (figs. 59-61).

Body rotund; girdle wider on dorsal side; girdle list funnel-shaped, supported by several strong ribs; left sulcal list lobed (three to four lobes), last rib ending at point of final lobe. Length 40-80 μ. Very similar to *O. steini*, differing in lobed sulcal list.

Pacific Ocean. Santaren Channel, Straits of Florida; Bahama Banks; Benguela Current; Caribbean Sea.

Genus OXYTOXUM Stein

Cell elongated, clavate to fusiform; girdle anterior, usually deep and broad; hypotheca and epitheca often acute with single antapical spine; no apical pore; ventral area short, often reduced; plate formula 5', Oa, 5'', 5''', Op.

Fig. 246

Oxytoxum belgicae Meunier, 1910

Meunier, 1910, p. 55, pl. 16, figs. 38-41; Wood, 1963a, p. 44, fig. 159.

Body suborbicular with obtusely angled apex and subacute antapex which is slightly spined; epitheca low, conical; girdle deep, displaced one width; hypotheca slightly swollen below girdle, plate sutures well marked; plates finely punctate. Length 60 μ.

Kara Sea; Coral Sea. Santaren Channel, Straits of Florida; Benguela Current; Brazil (north coast); Caribbean Sea.

Fig. 247

Oxytoxum caudatum Schiller, 1937

Schiller, 1937, p. 454, fig. 504; Wood, 1963a, p. 44, fig. 160.

Epitheca domed, small, with small apical spinule; girdle wide and deep; hypotheca wider than epitheca, tapering to acute antapex. Length 90 μ.

Eastern tropical Pacific Ocean; Coral and north Tasman seas. Straits of Florida.

Fig. 248

Oxytoxum challengeroides Kofoid, 1907

Kofoid, 1907b, p. 187, pl. 10 fig. 65.

Epitheca conical with concave margins tapering into a central horn; girdle wide and deep; hypotheca top-shaped with convex margins and antapical spine; sulcus about one-third length of hypotheca. Length 80-100 μ.

Tropical Pacific Ocean. Straits of Florida.

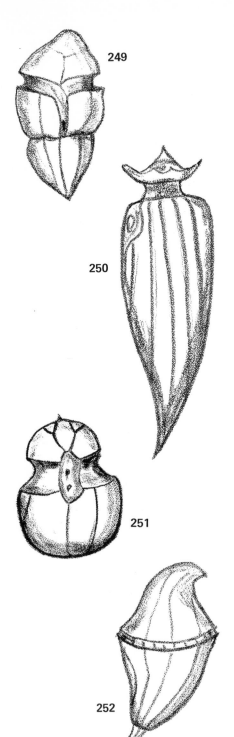

Fig. 249

Oxytoxum constrictum (Stein) Bütschli, 1885

Bütschli, 1885, p. 1006, pl. 53 (fig. 5); Wood, 1963*a*, p. 44, fig. 163.

Epitheca bluntly conical, apex rounded, sides concave; hypotheca conical with convex margins, constricted near the upper third and with a short, sharp spine. Length 75 μ.

Mediterranean Sea; Coral Sea. Santaren Channel, Straits of Florida; Benguela Current; Caribbean Sea.

Fig. 250

Oxytoxum coronatum Schiller, 1937

Schiller, 1937, p. 454, fig. 503; Wood, 1963*a*, p. 45, fig. 164.

Epitheca small, cap-shaped, with a short conical spinule; girdle broad and deep, forming a wing on the upper side suggesting a crown; hypotheca tapering to acute antapex, with longitudinal stripes. Length 40-45 μ.

Adriatic Sea; Indian Ocean. Straits of Florida.

Fig. 251

Oxytoxum crassum Schiller, 1937

Schiller, 1937, p. 459, fig. 518.

Epitheca small, rounded, with small apical spinule; hypotheca almost hemispherical with a short antapical spinule; girdle very broad; sulcus obvious in girdle region, only minimal on epitheca and hypotheca, plates marked. Length about 20 μ.

Adriatic Sea. Straits of Florida.

Fig. 252

Oxytoxum cristatum Kofoid, 1907

Kofoid, 1907*b*, p. 188, pl. 10 (fig. 64); Schiller, 1937, p. 463, fig. 528.

Body irregularly biconical, apex sharply bent at right angles to longitudinal axis, base bent at lesser angle in opposite direction with winged spine; epitheca and hypotheca subequal; girdle ribbed, slightly anterior. Length 100 μ.

Tropical waters; eastern Pacific Ocean. Caribbean Sea.

Fig. 253

Oxytoxum curvatum (Kofoid) Kofoid, 1911

Kofoid, 1911, p. 287; *Prorocentrum curvatum* Kofoid, 1907*b*, p. 166, pl. 1 (figs. 1-2).
Epitheca shortly cylindrical; hypotheca with blunt apical region, parallel sides curving to the tapering antapex. Length 60-100 μ.
Atlantic and Indian oceans; Pacific Ocean. Brazil (north coast); Caribbean Sea.

Fig. 254

Oxytoxum diploconus Stein, 1883

Stein, 1883, pl. 5 (fig. 5); Schiller, 1937, p. 463, fig. 529; Wood, 1954, p. 315, fig. 247.
Epitheca short and pointed, with concave sides; hypotheca long and pointed; theca with numerous longitudinal ribs and pores. Length 60-160 μ.
Tropical Atlantic Ocean; Mediterranean Sea; Port Jackson. Gulf Stream; Straits of Florida.

Fig. 255

Oxytoxum elegans Pavillard, 1916

Pavillard, 1916, p. 43, pl. 2 (fig. 4); Schiller, 1937, p. 464, fig. 530; Wood, 1963*a*, p. 45, fig. 167.
Epitheca shallow-conical with a short, acute pointed spine; girdle displaced one width; hypotheca deep, rounded with a short, abrupt pointed spine; striae at right angles to plate margins. Length 60-80 μ.
Mediterranean Sea; Indian Ocean; Coral and Tasman seas. Straits of Florida; Caribbean Sea.

Fig. 256

Oxytoxum elongatum Wood, 1963

Wood, 1963*a*, p. 45, fig. 168.
Body very elongate; epitheca rounded, with longish spine, but much smaller than hypotheca; hypotheca elongate, tapering with angular shoulders at girdle, and with a posterior spine. Length 150-200 μ.
Coral Sea; Vitiaz Strait; off New Ireland. Caribbean Sea.

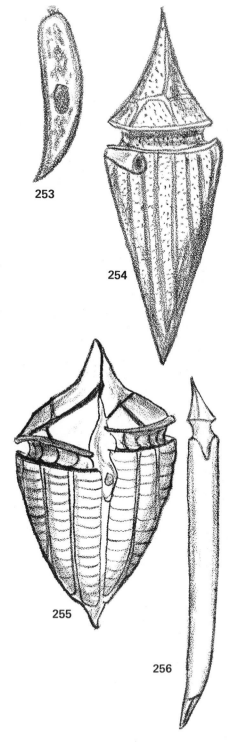

253

254

255

256

Fig. 257

Oxytoxum gladiolus Stein, 1883

Stein, 1883, pl. 5 (figs. 6-7); Schiller, 1937, p. 453, fig. 501a-b.

Epitheca rounded, small; girdle deep; hypotheca much wider than epitheca, conical with slight bend and acute, spined antapex; sutures marked. Length 50-75 μ.

Warm Atlantic Ocean and Mediterranean Sea. Sargasso Sea (Hulburt, 1962).

Fig. 258

Oxytoxum globosum Schiller, 1937

Schiller, 1937, p. 458, fig. 515a-b; Wood, 1963b, p. 16, fig. 59.

Epitheca low, elliptical, with or without a tiny spinule; girdle strongly constricted, moderately indented; hypotheca spherical with a small antapical spinule; sulcus small. Length 20-35 μ.

Adriatic Sea; eastern Indian Ocean. Straits of Florida.

Fig. 259

Oxytoxum gracile Schiller, 1937

Schiller, 1937, p. 455, fig. 506.

Epitheca conical, pointed with concave margins; girdle narrow, varying in depth; hypotheca with wide shoulders tapering to antapical spine; sulcus short. Length 25-30 μ.

Adriatic Sea; southwest Pacific Ocean. Brazil (north coast); Caribbean Sea.

Fig. 260

Oxytoxum laticeps Schiller, 1937

Schiller, 1937, p. 461, fig. 523; Wood, 1954, p. 46, fig. 170.

Body small, top-shaped; epitheca hemispherical; girdle deep, even; hypotheca truncate-ovate with antapical spine. Length 25 μ.

Adriatic Sea; Coral Sea; Indian Ocean. Straits of Florida; Caribbean Sea.

Fig. 261

Oxytoxum longiceps Schiller, 1937

Schiller, 1937, p. 464, fig. 532; Wood, 1963*a*, p. 46, fig. 171.

Epitheca conical, tapering into a long, acute spine; girdle very deep and wide; sulcus extending about girdle width on both epitheca and hypotheca; hypotheca tapering, curved; striae longitudinal on epitheca, hypotheca, and girdle. Length 50-60 μ.

Adriatic Sea; Coral Sea. Straits of Florida; Caribbean Sea.

Fig. 262

Oxytoxum mediterraneum Schiller, 1937

Schiller, 1937, p. 459, fig. 516.

Epitheca low, rounded, flattened apex; hypotheca cordate; girdle broad and deep, striate; sulcus from apex to about girdle width on hypotheca, broad; surface with hexagonal pores in rows. Length 24 μ.

Adriatic Sea. Straits of Florida.

Fig. 263

Oxytoxum milneri Murray and Whitting, 1899

Murray and Whitting, 1899, p. 328, pl. 27 (fig. 6); Wood, 1963*a*, p. 46, fig. 173.

Epitheca low, broadly conical, then tapering into a long, asymmetrical point; hypotheca deep, conical with convex margins, then forming an acute point; plates areolate with ridged sutures. Length 125-130 μ.

Tropical and subtropical waters in all oceans and seas. Santaren Channel, Straits of Florida; Benguela Current; Brazil (north coast); Caribbean Sea.

Fig. 264

Oxytoxum mitra (Stein) Schiller, 1937

Schiller, 1937, p. 459, fig. 517; Wood, 1963*a*, p. 48, fig. 174; *Pyrgidium mitra* Stein, 1883, pl. 5 (fig. 22), pl. 6 (fig. 1).

Epitheca hemispherical, with a small, blunt process; girdle moderate; hypotheca top-shaped, with a small antapical process. Length 70 μ.

Mediterranean and Coral seas. Straits of Florida.

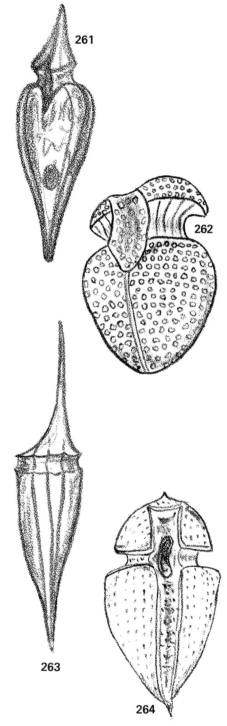

265

Fig. 265

Oxytoxum obliquum Schiller, 1937

Schiller, 1937, p. 457, fig. 513; Wood, 1963a, p. 48, fig. 175.

Epitheca with a rounded margin and blunt process slightly offset from longitudinal axis of cell; girdle of varying width; hypotheca subconical with rounded anterior margin and acute posterior, ending in a small spine. Length 50-60 μ.

Southern Adriatic and Coral seas. Straits of Florida; Caribbean Sea.

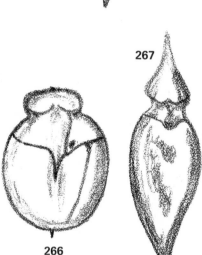

267

266

Fig. 266

Oxytoxum pachyderme Schiller, 1937

Schiller, 1937, p. 460, fig. 519.

Body rotund; epitheca low, rounded, with slight spine; hypotheca much larger, almost spherical; girdle wide, anterior; sulcus about half body length. Length 35-50 μ.

Adriatic and Coral seas. Brazil (north coast).

Fig. 267

Oxytoxum parvum Schiller, 1937

Schiller, 1937, p. 464, fig. 531; Wood, 1963a, p. 48, fig. 177.

Body biconical; epitheca much smaller than hypotheca, pointed, sides concave; girdle wide and deep, angled; hypotheca with margin convex below girdle, then tapering to a spine. Length 35-40 μ.

Adriatic Sea; Indian Ocean; Coral and Tasman seas. Straits of Florida; Caribbean Sea.

268

Fig. 268

Oxytoxum robustum Kofoid, 1911

Kofoid, 1911a, p. 288; Wood, 1963a, p. 48, fig. 178.

Epitheca dome-shaped, apex rounded; girdle moderate; hypotheca horn-shaped, bent at antapex with antapical spine. Length 100 μ.

California coast; Coral and north Tasman seas. Straits of Florida.

Fig. 269

Oxytoxum sceptrum (Stein) Schröder, 1906

Schröder, 1906, p. 327; Schiller, 1937, p. 458, fig. 514; Wood, 1963a, p. 49, fig. 179; *Pyrgidium sceptrum* Stein, 1883, pl. 5 (figs. 19-21).

Epitheca more or less globiform with a conspicuous, acute spine; girdle deep, varying in width; hypotheca wider than epitheca, sides convex, tapering to antapical spine. Length 75-90 μ.

Indian Ocean; Pacific Ocean. Straits of Florida; Caribbean Sea.

Fig. 270

Oxytoxum scolopax Stein, 1883

Stein, 1883, pl. 5 (figs. 1-3); Wood, 1954, p. 315, fig. 245.

Epitheca pyriform, with rounded part below and a spine above; hypotheca very long, somewhat bent, obliquely conical; antapical with a bladder-shaped endpiece and spine; theca with pores in longitudinal rows or striped; intercalary lines usually well marked. Length 70-120 μ.

Interoceanic warm-water species. West Channel, Straits of Florida; Benguela Current; Sargasso Sea (Hulburt, 1963); Gulf of Mexico (Curl, 1959); Brazil (north coast); Caribbean Sea.

Fig. 271

Oxytoxum sphaeroideum Stein, 1883

Stein, 1883, pl. 5, fig. 9; Wood, 1963a, p. 49, fig. 180.

Epitheca rotund; hypotheca ovate; antapex acute to rounded; girdle wide and deep; sulcus short. Length 30-50 μ.

Widespread in warm water. Straits of Florida; Sargasso Sea; Gulf Stream; Bermuda (Hulburt, 1963); Caribbean Sea.

Fig. 272

Oxytoxum subulatum Kofoid, 1907

Kofoid, 1907b, p. 190, pl. 10 (fig. 62); Schiller, 1937, p. 465, fig. 535; Wood, 1954, p. 316, fig. 250.

Epitheca low and broad, with a long, cylindrical process, truncated at apex; hypotheca tapering with convex sides to a fine antapical spine; girdle and sulcus deeply indented; surface of hypotheca with ten to twelve parallel longitudinal striae. Length 120-150 μ.

Tropical Pacific Ocean. Straits of Florida.

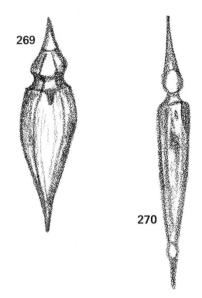

269

270

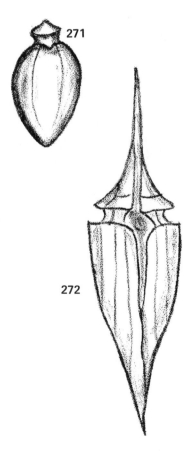

271

272

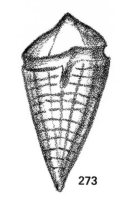

Fig. 273

Oxytoxum tesselatum (Stein) Schütt, 1895

Schütt, 1895, p. 160, pl. 17 (fig. 52); Schiller, 1937, p. 462, fig. 526a-b.

Epitheca conical, low; hypotheca top-shaped, ending in an antapical spinule; girdle deep, moderately wide; hypotheca surface with rectangular meshes. Length 60 μ.

Sargasso Sea (Hulburt, 1963); Straits of Florida; Brazil (north coast); Caribbean Sea.

Fig. 274

Oxytoxum turbo Kofoid, 1907

Kofoid, 1907*b*, p. 190, pl. 10 (fig. 60); Wood, 1954, p. 315, fig. 246.

Epitheca hemispherical with a short, thick spinelet; hypotheca long, swollen below girdle, pointed at base; theca longitudinally striate. Length 40-60 μ.

Tropical Pacific Ocean. Santaren Channel, Straits of Florida; Benguela Current; Brazil (north coast); Caribbean Sea.

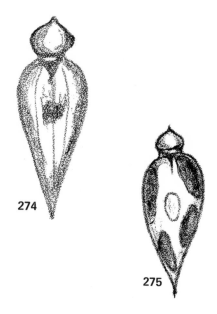

Fig. 275

Oxytoxum variabile Schiller, 1937

Schiller, 1937, p. 455, fig. 505; Wood, 1963*a*, p. 49, fig. 183.

Epitheca hemispherical to broadly conical with a short, fine spinule; hypotheca more or less cordate or top-shaped, ending in a fine spinule; girdle narrow; sulcus long, only on hypotheca. Length 20-25 μ.

Adriatic Sea; southwest Pacific Ocean. Santaren Channel, Straits of Florida; Benguela Current; Sargasso Sea (Hulburt, 1963); Bermuda (Hulburt, 1963); Gulf Stream (Hulburt, 1963); Venezuela (Hulburt, 1963); Brazil (north coast); Caribbean Sea.

Fig. 276

Oxytoxum viride Schiller, 1937

Schiller, 1937, p. 456, fig. 510b.

Epitheca low, rounded; hypotheca subspherical, slightly cordate, with antapical spinule; girdle rather deep; sulcus small. Length 20 μ.

Adriatic Sea. Straits of Florida.

Genus PARAHISTIONEIS Kofoid and Skogsberg

Body rotund, gourd-shaped, porulate, usually slightly longer than wide; epitheca small; girdle wider dorsally than ventrally; anterior girdle list flared and strongly ribbed; posterior list forming a cylindrical collar with less than six radial ribs and without submarginal cross-rib; left sulcal list large with single posterior lobe and one complete rib behind fission rib.

Fig. 277

Parahistioneis acuta Bohm, 1931

Bohm, 1931, in Schiller, 1933, p. 216, fig. 206.

Body ovate; epitheca elevated toward ventral side; hypotheca hemispherical, coarsely porulate; anterior girdle list wide, flared, ribbed; posterior slightly flared, hyaline; sulcal list narrow at R_2, widening toward R_3 which is ventral; R_2 becoming posterior as margin of sulcal list and uniting with R_3 to form a point. Length 75-80 μ.

Indian and tropical Atlantic oceans. Rare in Straits of Florida.

Fig. 278

Parahistioneis crateriformis (Stein) Kofoid and Skogsberg, 1928

Kofoid and Skogsberg, 1928, p. 590; *Histioneis crateriformis* Stein, 1883, pl. 22, figs. 5-6.

Hypotheca semicircular; epitheca conical with concave sides; girdle broad; anterior girdle list flared; posterior list of even width, cylindrical; left sulcal list with sigmoid margin ending ventrally of median line. Length 50-60 μ.

Atlantic Ocean; southwest Pacific Ocean. Brazil (north coast).

Fig. 279

Parahistioneis gascoynensis Wood, 1963

Wood, 1963a, pl. 13, fig. 37.

Body rotund; epitheca low, higher dorsally; anterior girdle list broadly flaring, strongly ribbed; posterior list low, hyaline; left sulcal list narrow to R_2, which is deflected posteriorly, then wider and rounded to R_3, which is posteroventral and ribbed. Length 50-70 μ.

Coral Sea. Brazil (north coast).

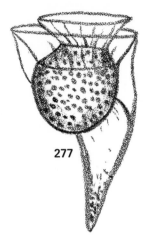

277

278

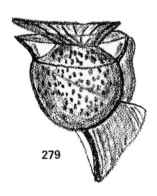

279

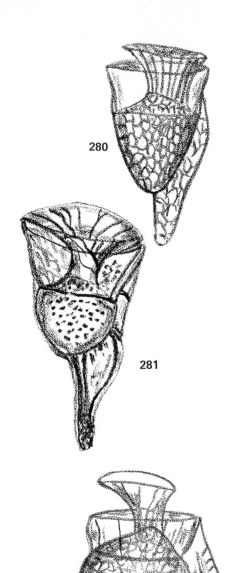

Fig. 280

Parahistioneis para Murray and Whitting, 1899

Murray and Whitting, 1899, pl. 32 (fig. 4a-b); Kofoid and Skogsberg, 1928, p. 601, figs. 85-86.

Body somewhat ovate; girdle deep and wide, of even width; anterior girdle list funnel-shaped, evenly ribbed; posterior girdle list with few ribs; sulcal list narrow, ventral, widening posteriorly; R_3 long, ventral, with thickening at end. Length 40-50 μ.

Santaren Channel, Straits of Florida; Benguela Current.

Fig. 281

Parahistioneis paraformis Kofoid and Skogsberg, 1928

Kofoid and Skogsberg, 1928, p. 598, fig. 19 (3-6), pl. 93 (fig. 4); Wood, 1963a, p. 13, fig. 38.

Body rotund; girdle wide; anterior girdle list funnel-shaped, ribbed; posterior girdle list with few ribs; left sulcal list with rounded margin ending at R_3, which is slightly ventral; list granular in antapical part. Length 40-50 μ.

Tropical and subtropical Pacific Ocean. Straits of Florida.

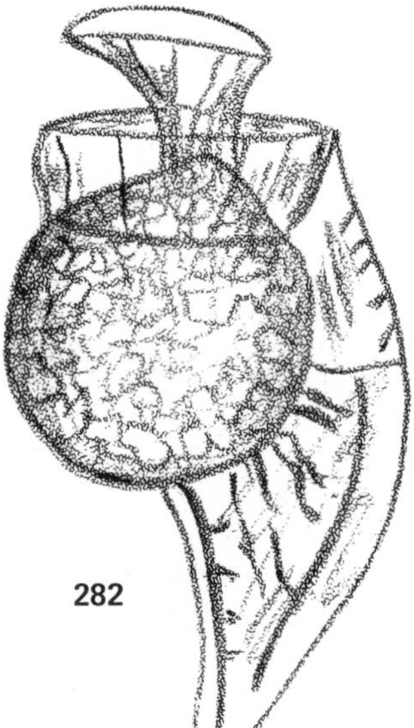

Fig. 282

Parahistioneis rotundata (Kofoid and Michener) Kofoid and Skogsberg, 1928

Kofoid and Skogsberg, 1928, p. 593, fig. 93, pl. 19 (figs. 8-9); *Histioneis rotundata* Kofoid and Michener, 1911, p. 299.

Body rotund; epitheca tapering; anterior girdle list funnel-shaped, strongly ribbed; posterior list slightly flaring, ribbed; left sulcal list with undulate ventral margin, supported by R_3, which is slightly ventral but directed posteriorly; R_2 has a branch running submarginally but not reaching R_3. Length 20-30 μ.

Tropical Pacific and Atlantic oceans. Straits of Florida.

Genus PERIDINIUM Ehrenberg

Body polygonal to rotund, often flattened
to curved laterally; epitheca and hypotheca
more or less equal; girdle may be depressed
or not, with or without lists; sulcus usually
with lists which may extend beyond antapex;
apical horn may be "affixed" or tapering,
long or rudimentary; antapical spines may be
present or antapex may extend into two antapical processes; plate formula variable.

Glenodinium and possibly *Diplopsalis*
should be united with this genus.

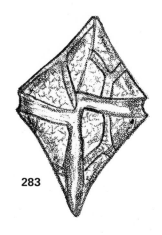

283

Fig. 283

Peridinium abei Paulsen, 1930

Paulsen, 1930, p. 73; Schiller, 1937, p. 138,
fig. 136a-h; Wood, 1954, p. 229, fig. 91.

Cell biconical, longer than broad; epitheca
approximately equal to hypotheca, left-
handed; girdle indented with narrow lists;
sulcus deep, curving to left, ending on left
margin of hypotheca; surface often porulate;
ortho; two intercalary plates. Length 70-
100 μ.

Estuarine species; Japan; Indian and Pacific
oceans. Straits of Florida.

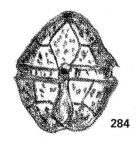

284

Fig. 284

Peridinium avellana (Meunier) Lebour, 1925

Lebour, 1925, p. 108, pl. 17 (fig. 1); *Proper-
idinium avellana* Meunier, 1919, p. 56, pl. 18,
figs. 37-41.

Body suborbicular; epitheca and hypotheca
equal, sides straight or slightly concave, ends
rounded; girdle depressed; base slightly indentate. Length 35 μ.

English Channel; Coral Sea. Brazil (north
coast).

Fig. 285

Peridinium biconicum Dangeard, 1927

Dangeard, 1927, p. 11, fig. 7; Schiller, 1937,
p. 230, fig. 227a-e.

Theca biconical, apex and antapex acute,
no apical horn or spines; ortho, hexa; girdle
depressed, not displaced; sulcus broad, not
reaching antapex. Length 80-100 μ.

Atlantic, Indian, and Pacific oceans; Persian
Gulf. Straits of Florida.

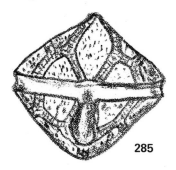

285

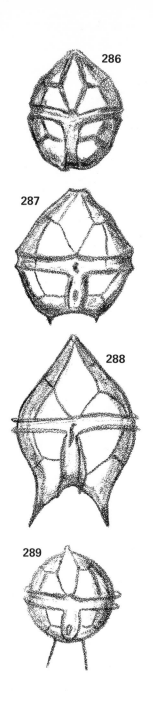

286

287

288

289

Body subrotund, sides irregular; apical horn short; hypotheca rounded, base slightly indentate; girdle right-handed, slightly depressed; sulcus broad with inconspicuous lists ending in small winged spines. Length 45-75 μ.

Neritic from boreal waters to Antarctic; Pacific and Atlantic oceans. Brazil (north coast).

Fig. 287

Peridinium brevipes Paulsen, 1908

Paulsen, 1908, p. 108, fig. 151; Wood, 1954, p. 241, fig. 122.

Cell somewhat rhombic in outline with rounded ends and conical apex; girdle right-handed, excavated, with very narrow lists; sulcus broadening toward antapex ending in two small spines which may be absent; tabulation meta, quadra. Length 30-45 μ.

Cold water in North Sea and Baltic Sea; estuarine in Australia; Antarctic waters. Straits of Florida; Brazil (north coast).

Fig. 288

Peridinium brochi Kofoid and Swezy, 1921

Kofoid and Swezy, 1921, p. 183; Wood, 1954, p. 247, fig. 136.

Cell variable, slightly longer than broad; epitheca with convex margins tapering into a conical apical horn; hypotheca with sigmoid margins ending in two slightly divergent antapicals; base strongly concave; girdle not depressed, with hyaline lists; sulcus with lists, reaching base; tabulation meta, quadra. Length 100 μ.

Atlantic Ocean; Mediterranean Sea; Pacific Ocean. Caribbean Sea.

Fig. 289

Peridinium cerasus Paulsen, 1907

Paulsen, 1907, p. 12, fig. 12.

Cells spherical with conspicuous, fairly long apical horn; girdle slightly right-handed; two antapical spines not at margins of sulcus but asymmetrically at a distance from it; theca punctate; precingular 1'' very small in contrast with large 7''; meta, quadra. Length 30-40 μ. Not identical with *P. globulus* as stated by Schiller, 1937.

Estuarine-neritic species. Straits of Florida; Benguela Current; Brazil (north coast); Caribbean Sea.

Fig. 286

Peridinium breve Paulsen, 1907

Paulsen, 1907, p. 13; Wood, 1954, p. 241, fig. 121a-d.

Fig. 290

Peridinium claudicans Paulsen, 1907

Paulsen, 1907, p. 16, fig. 22; Wood, 1954, p. 255, fig. 154.

Epitheca with convex sides, tapering into a conical apical horn; girdle not depressed, slightly offset; hypotheca convex with two acute antapicals but without spines; ortho, quadra; girdle lists conspicuous. Length 50-100 μ.

Neritic species in all oceans. Straits of Florida.

Fig. 291

Peridinium conicoides Paulsen, 1905

Paulsen, 1905, p. 3, fig. 2; Wood, 1954, p. 250, fig. 145.

Cell in ventral view somewhat rhombic with weakly convex sides; girdle slightly offset, narrow list; epitheca almost domed, tapering into slight apical horn; hypotheca equal to epitheca with two small, hollow antapicals; sulcus broadening posteriorly; ortho, hexa. Length 50-60 μ.

Arctic Ocean, Antarctic waters, east coast of Australia. Fowey Rocks.

Fig. 292

Peridinium conicum (Gran) Ostenfeld and Schmidt, 1901

Ostenfeld and Schmidt, 1901, p. 174; Gran, 1902, pp. 185, 189, fig. 14.

Epitheca conical, sides almost straight; hypotheca equal to epitheca with biconical antapex; girdle slightly concave, even; sulcus even, reaching indented base; spines absent; intercalary striae often broad; theca finely reticulate; ortho, hexa. Length 70-80 μ.

Estuarine-neritic species. Amazon estuary.

Fig. 293

Peridinium crassipes Kofoid, 1907

Kofoid, 1907*a*, p. 309, pl. 31, figs. 46, 47; Wood, 1954, p. 247, fig. 137a-d.

Body low and stout, slightly flattened dorsoventrally with reniform girdle section; main axis deflected anterodorsally; epitheca with convex sides and tapering apical horn; hypotheca convex with right antapical longer than left; meta, quadra. Length 80-100 μ.

Estuarine-neritic in all oceans. Straits of Florida.

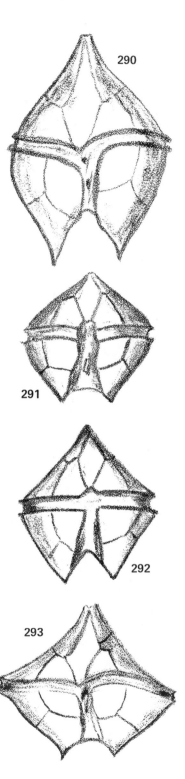

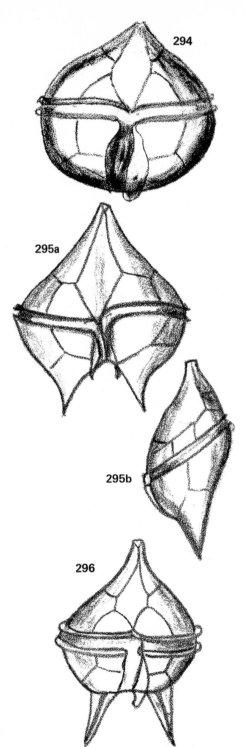

Fig. 294

Peridinium curvipes Ostenfeld, 1906

Ostenfeld, 1906, p. 15, fig. 128; Wood, 1954, p. 242, fig. 124.

Body rounded-oval, tapering to apical horn; base rounded; girdle broadly winged, right-handed; left sulcal list with broad wing, evenly curved posteriorly toward antapex; right list narrower, ending in a small spine; plate arrangement very variable. Length 44-55 μ.

Estuarine-neritic species, wide range of occurrence. Straits of Florida.

Fig. 295 a-b

Peridinium depressum Bailey, 1855

Bailey, 1855, p. 12, figs. 33-34; Wood, 1954, p. 255, fig. 155a-b.

Cell broad, obliquely flattened dorso-ventrally; axis very oblique; epitheca tapering into large apical horn; hypotheca with two long, tapering antapicals, each with a spinelet continuous with the sulcal list; girdle left-handed, offset; theca reticulate. (a. front view; b. side view.) Length 100-200 μ.

Euryhaline and eurythermal, found from Antarctic to Arctic waters. Straits of Florida; Benguela Current; Gulf Stream (Hulburt, 1963); west coast of Florida (Curl, 1959); Brazil (north coast); Caribbean Sea.

Fig. 296

Peridinium diabolus Cleve, 1900

Cleve, 1900, p. 16, pl. 7 (figs. 19-20); Wood, 1954, p. 243, fig. 125.

Body rounded, little contracted dorso-ventrally; epitheca with sigmoid margins; apical horn moderate; hypotheca rounded with concave base; girdle slightly right-handed or circular, not hollow, lists supported by spines; sulcus widening below, left list ending in spinelet connected with winged antapical spine; right antapical spine winged, equal to left antapical. Length 80-180 μ.

Warm waters of all oceans; Antarctic convergence. Pigeon Key; Brazil (north coast); Caribbean Sea.

Fig. 297

Peridinium divaricatum Meunier, 1919

Meunier, 1919, p. 48, pl. 19 (figs. 55-58); Wood, 1954, p. 251, fig. 147.

Epitheca an isosceles triangle; girdle depressed, with more or less strongly developed lists; hypotheca with straight sides ending in two divergent antapicals with or without spines; sulcus widening to base. Length 50 μ.

Brackish water on Belgian, English, and east Australian coasts. Straits of Florida.

Fig. 298

Peridinium divergens Ehrenberg, 1840

Ehrenberg, 1840, p. 201; Wood, 1954, p. 248, fig. 139.

Very variable; cells longer than broad, with two hollow antapicals, sides of epitheca and hypotheca concave; girdle right-handed, slightly offset and excavated; lists conspicuous, supported by spines; sulcal list extending into spinelets at bases of antapicals. Length 60-100 μ.

Interoceanic, euryhaline. Bahama Banks; Fowey Rocks; Benguela Current; Brazil (north coast); Florida Everglades; Caribbean Sea.

Fig. 299

Peridinium excentricum Paulsen, 1907

Paulsen, 1907, p. 14, fig. 17; Wood, 1954, p. 229, fig. 94a-b.

Cell depressed, very much obliquely twisted so that the left side of the hypotheca is larger than the right; epitheca flattened with tapering apical horn; hypotheca flattened with an antapical process on left; girdle with lists, depressed; sulcus deep, reaching antapex. Length 35 μ.

North Sea, Mediterranean Sea; Indian and Pacific oceans. Straits of Florida.

Fig. 300

Peridinium fatulipes Kofoid, 1907

Kofoid, 1907a, p. 175, pl. 5, fig. 30; Wood, 1963a, p. 36, fig. 131.

Body much widened at girdle; epitheca conical, sides more or less concave, tapering into a rather long apical horn; hypotheca trapezoidal with antapical horns strongly diverging, about equal in length to apical, and may be spinulate; meta, quadra. Length 150-

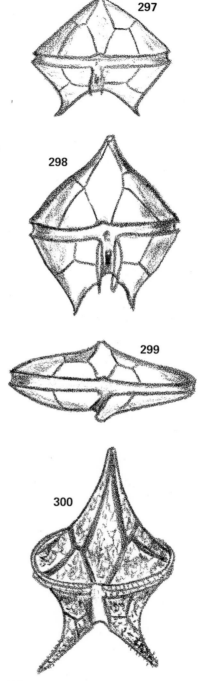

$200\,\mu$.

Tropical seas; Indian Ocean. Straits of Florida; Caribbean Sea.

101

301a

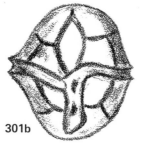

301b

Fig. 301 a-b

Peridinium gatunense Nygaard, 1925

Ostenfeld and Nygaard, 1925, p. 206; Wood, 1954, p. 232, fig. 102.

Cell ovate, somewhat angular; apical flattened, rounded; hypotheca lower than epitheca; girdle displaced, depressed, ribbed; sulcus not reaching antapex, which has a small process. (a. front view; b. side view.) Length 45-80 μ.

Central America, France, and Africa. Florida Everglades in fresh water; Key Largo in epilithic felts.

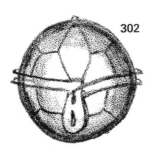

302

Fig. 302

Peridinium globulus Stein, 1883

Stein, 1883, pl. 9 (figs. 5-7); Wood, 1954, p. 236, fig. 110.

Cell globular or lenticulate with a very short, affixed apical horn; girdle strongly right-handed, not excavated, lists supported by spines; sulcus narrow, extending to epitheca, with inconspicuous lists; no antapical spines; meta, hexa (hepta). Length 50-70 μ.

Interoceanic warm-water species. Straits of Florida; Benguela Current; Sargasso Sea; Bermuda (Hulburt, 1963); Brazil (north coast).

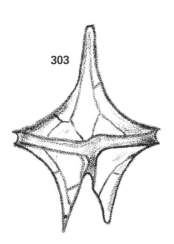

303

Fig. 303

Peridinium grande Kofoid, 1907

Kofoid, 1907*b*, p. 174, pl. 5 (fig. 28); Wood, 1954, p. 249, fig. 142.

A very large species of the *divergens* group, with flaring girdle and long horns; girdle median, narrow, slightly left-handed, depressed, ribbed; sides of theca deeply concave; antapicals slightly unequal, divergent, conical, acute; sulcus with membranous list extending beyond base. Length 150-200 μ.

Tropical, interoceanic. Straits of Florida; Benguela Current; Caribbean Sea.

Fig. 304

Peridinium grani Ostenfeld, 1906

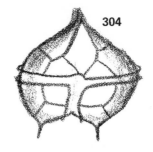
304

Ostenfeld, 1906; Paulsen, 1907, p. 15, fig. 18; Wood, 1954, p. 238, fig. 116a-c.

Very variable form; sides sigmoid; epitheca tapering into apical horn; hypotheca tapering into two hollow antapicals which are divergent; these may be replaced by spines; girdle offset, depressed, with moderate lists; sulcus variable with moderate lists. Length 40-100 μ.

Largely neritic, pelagic in the Antarctic. Benguela Current; Caribbean Sea.

Fig. 305

Peridinium gymnodinium (Penard), 1891

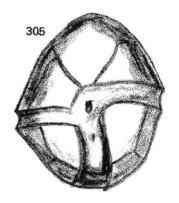
305

Penard, 1891, p. 54, pl. 4 (figs. 8-10).

Body ovate, apex and base rounded; left sulcal list narrow but may be prolonged as a small spinelet; girdle recessed, left handed, displaced nearly one width; sulcus even or slightly flaring. Length 40 μ.

Frequent in fresh and brackish water in Europe. Florida Everglades.

Fig. 306

Peridinium hirobis Abé, 1927

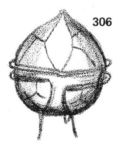
306

Abé, 1927, p. 399, fig. 18a-e; Wood, 1954, p. 243, fig. 126.

Rounded cell with small, tapering apical horn; girdle right-handed, slightly or not depressed; lists wide; sulcus wide, with lists, of which the right is continuous with an unwinged antapical, the left with a wide wing projecting below body; tabulation para (meta), hexa. Length 25-50 μ.

Estuarine-neritic species; Japanese coast; east Australia. Straits of Florida. Caribbean Sea.

Fig. 307

Peridinium inconspicuum Lemmermann, 1899

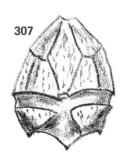
307

Lemmermann, 1899, p. 350; Schiller, 1937, p. 173, fig. 175a-w, z.

Body ovate, with somewhat angular sides; epitheca subconical, larger than hypotheca; girdle even or slightly left-handed, depressed; hypotheca low, with three or more spinelets along base, deepest in middle of sulcus where there is a spinelet; sulcus flaring. Length 15-30 μ.

Florida Everglades.

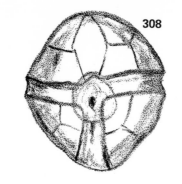

Fig. 308

Peridinium kulczynskii Woloszynska, 1916

Woloszynska, 1916, p. 272, pl. 12, figs. 25-31; *Glenodinium kulczynskii* Schiller, 1937, p. 96, fig. 82a-c.

Body broadly ovate; epitheca and hypotheca equal, rounded; no processes; girdle depressed, slightly offset; sulcus flaring, not on epitheca; plate arrangement 4' (3', 1a), 6", 6"', 2"". Length 35 μ.

Galicia. Florida Everglades in fresh water.

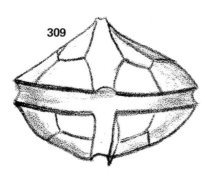

Fig. 309

Peridinium latum Paulsen, 1908

Paulsen, 1908, p. 41, fig. 48; Wood, 1954, p. 233, fig. 103.

Epitheca regularly conical, sharply tapering to a short apical horn; hypotheca rounded antapically, often slightly flattened; plate formula 4', 1-2a, 7", 5"', 1"". Length 30-40 μ.

European and Australian ponds and lakes and in brackish water. Florida Everglades.

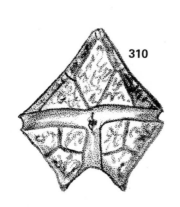

Fig. 310

Peridinium leonis Pavillard, 1916

Pavillard, 1916, p. 32, fig. 6; Wood, 1954, p. 251, fig. 148a-c.

Cell rhombic, margins of epitheca and hypotheca straight or slightly concave; epitheca obliquely conical; hypotheca a truncated cone with indented base and two conical antapicals with small, blunt spines; girdle slightly left-handed, slightly indented, with lists; sulcus deep, reaching base; surface reticulate. Length 65-100 μ.

Atlantic, Pacific, and Indian oceans. Caribbean Sea.

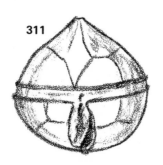

Fig. 311

Peridinium minutum Kofoid, 1907

Kofoid, 1907a, p. 310, pl. 31, figs. 42-45.

Body rotund, with small, tapering apical horn, base rounded without spines; girdle slightly or not depressed, even; sulcus with lists, left list projecting beyond base; ortho, hexa. Length 40-60 μ.

Pacific and Atlantic oceans; temperate estuaries and inshore areas. Straits of Florida.

Fig. 312

Peridinium murrayi Kofoid, 1907

Kofoid, 1907*b*, p. 176, pl. 5 (fig. 29); Wood, 1954, p. 256, fig. 156.

Body small, rhomboidal; apical and antapical horns long, the latter strongly diverging, with a deep hollow between. Length 150-200 μ. Schiller, 1937, synonymises this species with *P. oceanicum.*

Tropical interoceanic species. Benguela Current.

Fig. 313

Peridinium oceanicum Vanhöffen, 1897

Vanhöffen, 1897, pl. 5 (fig. 2); Wood, 1954, p. 256, fig. 157a-b.

Cells elongate and oblique to vertical axis, flattened dorsoventrally; body rotund in outline tapering into long apical and antapical horns, without spines; girdle not depressed, straight or slightly left-handed, lists present; sulcus usually with lists on either side. Length 110-200 μ.

Oceanic and neritic species. Straits of Florida; Caribbean Sea.

Fig. 314

Peridinium okamurai Abé, 1927

Abé, 1927, p. 402, fig. 20; Wood, 1954, p. 243, fig. 127.

Cell elongated pyriform; epitheca subconical with convex sides and small, tapering apical horn; hypotheca rounded; girdle slightly or not depressed, with lists, right-handed; sulcus with lists, left with a projecting wing; two strong antapical spines, diverging; para, hexa. Length 60-75 μ.

Estuarine in Mutsu Bay (Japan) and Moreton Bay (Australia). Straits of Florida; Caribbean Sea.

Fig. 315

Peridinium orbiculare Paulsen, 1907

Paulsen, 1907, fig. 10; Paulsen, 1908, p. 42, fig. 50; Schiller, 1937, p. 141, fig. 141a-e.

Body rotund; epitheca convex, tapering into apical horn; hypotheca rounded; girdle depressed, with lists, straight; sulcus rounded at base with left wing projecting well below base. Length 50 μ.

North Sea; Baltic Sea; Iceland. Straits of Florida.

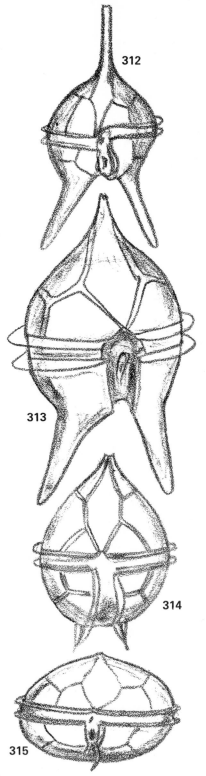

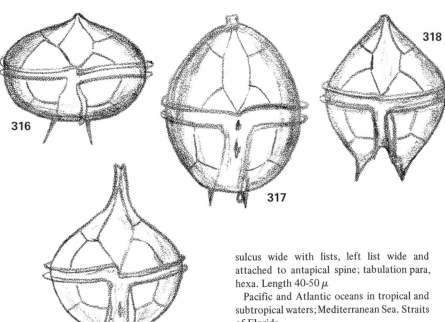

316

317

318

319

Fig. 316

Peridinium ovatum (Pouchet) Schütt, 1895

Schütt, 1895, pl. 16 (fig. 49); Wood, 1954, p. 236, fig. 112a-d; *Protoperidinium ovatum* Pouchet, 1883, p. 35, pl. 18 (fig. 13).

Cell lenticular; epitheca low, domed, tapering sharply to a small apical horn; hypotheca low, rounded, normally with two small antapical spines; girdle not depressed, slightly right-handed, lists supported by spines; sulcus subantapical or reaching base, lists present, left list extending posteriorly. Length 50-75μ.

Interoceanic, euryhaline species. Straits of Florida, not common.

Fig. 317

Peridinium ovum Schiller, 1911

Schiller, 1911, fig. 1a-d; Schiller, 1937, p. 208, fig. 205a-h; Wood, 1954, p. 244, fig. 128.

Cell oval, almost spherical with a short, affixed apical horn and two long winged or short unwinged antapical spines; girdle not depressed, lists supported by fine spines;

sulcus wide with lists, left list wide and attached to antapical spine; tabulation para, hexa. Length 40-50 μ

Pacific and Atlantic oceans in tropical and subtropical waters; Mediterranean Sea. Straits of Florida.

Fig. 318

Peridinium pallidum Ostenfeld, 1899

Ostenfeld, 1899, p. 60; Wood, 1954, p. 244, fig. 129a-b.

Cell flattened dorsoventrally, somewhat rhombic in ventral view, longer than broad; epitheca conical, sides straight or convex; hypotheca more or less rounded; girdle slightly right-handed or even, lists supported by spines; margins of sulcus extended into winged spines; para, hexa (quadra). Length about 80 μ.

Ubiquitous in neritic and estuarine environments. Straits of Florida.

Fig. 319

Peridinium pendunculatum Schütt, 1895

Schütt, 1895, pl. 14, fig. 47; Wood, 1954, p. 244, fig. 129a-b.

Similar to *P. steini* and *P. piriforme* but with more conical epitheca (higher than hypotheca), suddenly contracting into a long apical horn; girdle not offset, not depressed, lists moderate; sulcus expanding to base, winged; spines long, thin, winged. Length 30-50 μ.

Warm-water form, interoceanic. Straits of Florida; Benguela Current; Brazil (north coast); Caribbean Sea.

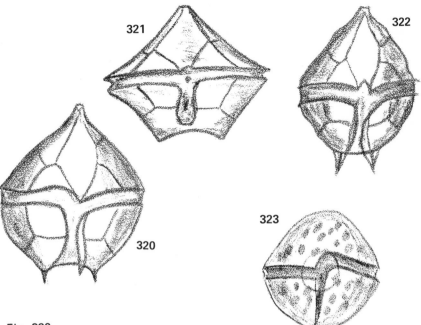

Fig. 320

Peridinium pellucidum (Bergh) Schütt, 1895

Schütt, 1895, pl. 14 (fig. 45); Schiller, 1937, p. 212, fig. 209a-w; *Protoperidinium pellucidum* Bergh, 1881.

Cells variable, very slightly flattened dorsoventrally, broadly oval, long axis perpendicular to girdle plane; margins convex; girdle not or slightly excavated, lists supported by spines; right margin of sulcus ending in one left and two antapical spines, all with or without hyaline wings; tabulation meta or para, hexa. Length 30-70 μ.

Estuarine. Fowey Rocks; Straits of Florida; Florida Everglades.

Fig. 321

Peridinium pentagonum Gran, 1902

Gran, 1902, pp. 185, 190, fig. 15; Wood, 1954, p. 253, fig. 150a.

Cell asymmetrical, pentagonal, contracted dorsoventrally; epitheca conical; hypotheca trapezoidal, margins straight or concave, base almost straight or concave; girdle depressed, slightly left-handed; sulcus not reaching base, rounded; ortho, hexa. Length 75-100 μ.

Estuarine-neritic form, widely distributed in all oceans. Straits of Florida.

Fig. 322

Peridinium piriforme Paulsen, 1904

Paulsen, 1904; Wood, 1954, p. 239, fig. 118.

Cells clumsily ovate; epitheca conical, almost rectilinear in outline; hypotheca dome-shaped, often with flattened sides and base; apical horn conical; girdle depressed, slightly right-handed; spines short, winged, wing on left spine continuous with sulcal list; tabulation meta, penta. Length 40-70 μ.

Cool-water form in Arctic and Antarctic waters, estuarine in southeast Australia. Fowey Rocks.

Fig. 323

Peridinium pulvisculus Ehrenberg, 1840

Ehrenberg, 1840, p. 253, pl. 22 (fig. 14); *Glenodinium pulvisculus* Stein, 1883, p. 3, figs. 8-17; Schiller, 1937, p. 95, fig. 80a-b.

Cell almost spherical, apex and base rounded; epitheca and hypotheca even; girdle displaced about one width, depressed; sulcus from girdle tapering to base; surface of theca hyaline. Length 25 μ.

European fresh waters. Florida Everglades.

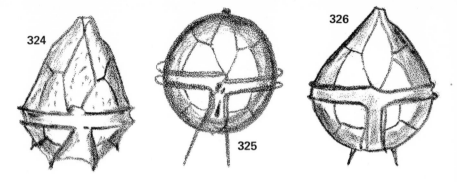

Fig. 324

Peridinium quadridens Stein, 1883

Stein, 1883, pl. 11 (figs. 3-6); *Glenodinium quadridens* Schiller, 1937, p. 117, fig. 115a-n. (For more extensive synonymy, see Schiller, *loc. cit.*).

Body angular; epitheca subconical with angled sides, higher than base; apical horn small, tapering; girdle even, depressed; sulcus flaring; two basal spines and frequently two more spines on hypotheca. Length 25-40 μ.

Cosmopolitan in fresh water. Florida Everglades.

Fig. 325

Peridinium quarnerense Schröder, 1910

Schröder, 1910; Wood, 1954, p. 236, fig. 111.

Cell globular, with small, "affixed" apical horn and two antapical spines, usually continuous with wide sulcal lists; girdle not indented, right-handed, with lists supported by spines; sulcal curved or straight, may reach base; plates meta, quadra or penta. Length 50-75 μ.

Interoceanic warm-water species. Pigeon Key; Santaren Channel, Straits of Florida; Brazil (north coast).

Fig. 326

Peridinium roseum (Paulsen) Paulsen, 1949

Paulsen, 1949.

Cell rounded or somewhat rhombic, tapering to short apical horn; girdle right-handed, not depressed, lists present; hypotheca rounded, even; sulcus broadening below, winged, wings not connected with two sharp antapical spines; meta, quadra. Length 30-45 μ.

Neritic species in Atlantic and Pacific oceans. Mouth of Amazon River.

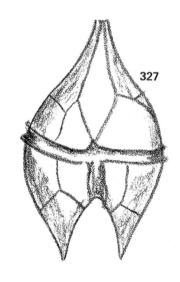

Fig. 327

Peridinium solidicorne Mangin, 1926

Mangin, 1926, p. 80, fig. 23; Wood, 1954, p. 247, fig. 135.

Body longer than broad; epitheca with convex sides tapering into a conical apical horn; hypotheca also convex, tapering into two solid spines which extend posteriorly or diverge; girdle even or slightly excavated, right-handed, lists supported by spines; sulcal lists wide, extending below base; tabulation para, quadra. Length 70-120 μ.

Widely distributed in all oceans. Straits of Florida.

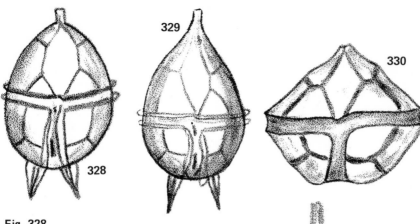

Fig. 328

Peridinium sphaericum Okamura, 1912

Okamura, 1912, p. 14, pl. 4 (figs. 71-72);
Schiller, 1937, p. 214, fig. 210a-f.

Cell spherical or slightly oval with affixed
apical horn and two winged antapical spines
set well ventrally; lists on both sides of sulcus
continuous with wings of spines; girdle right-
handed, not depressed, lists present; para,
quadra. Length 50 μ.

Tropical oceanic species. Amazon canyon
area.

Fig. 329

Peridinium steini Jörgensen, 1899

Jörgensen, 1899, p. 38; Wood, 1954, p. 240,
fig. 120.

Cell pear-shaped; epitheca and hypotheca
rounded, with tapering, elongated apical
horn; antapex with two broadly winged,
unequal spines, right larger than left. Length
40-100 μ.

Warm-water species in Atlantic and Pacific
oceans. West Channel, Santaren Channel,
Straits of Florida; Benguela Current; Brazil
(north coast); Caribbean Sea.

Fig. 330

Peridinium subinerme Paulsen, 1904

Paulsen, 1904, p. 24, fig. 10; Wood, 1954,
p. 254, fig. 151.

Cell nearly square; epitheca with weakly
convex sides; hypotheca with nearly straight
sides and indented base; apical horn continuous with sides, antapicals very slight; girdle
almost circular, excavated, lists with fine
spines; sulcus depressed, with ridged borders;
tabulation ortho, hexa, rarely penta. Length

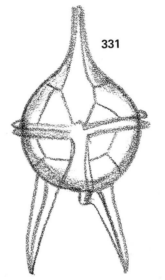

50-75 μ.

Boreal, Arctic and Antarctic waters. Benguela Current; Brazil (north coast); Caribbean
Sea.

Fig. 331

Peridinium tenuissimum Kofoid, 1907

Kofoid, 1907b, p. 176, pl. 5, fig. 34; Wood,
1954, p. 246, fig. 133.

Small, hyaline form with an elongated
ovate body, long apical horn, and antapical
spines; hypotheca rounded; antapical spines
equal in length to diameter of cell; girdle
even, right-handed, lists present; sulcus with
wide left list extending below base; meta,
penta. Length 25-30 μ.

Tropical oceanic waters in Pacific, Indian,
and Atlantic oceans. Straits of Florida.

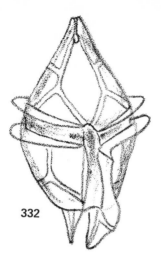

332

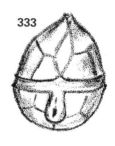

333

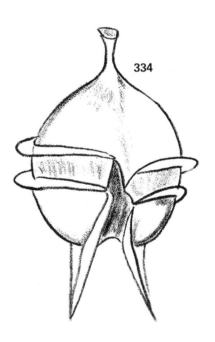

334

Fig. 332

Peridinium tristylum Stein, 1883

Stein, 1883, pl. 9 (figs. 15-17); Schiller, 1937, p. 216, fig. 212a-d.

Body elongate, somewhat flattened dorso-ventrally; epitheca acute, conical, tapering into conical apical horn; hypotheca truncate-conical with flat base, sides slightly concave or straight; girdle even, with lists supported by spines; sulcus with strong left list extending posteriorly and thickened, forming a third spine or attached to left antapical spine; tabulation para, hexa. Length 80 μ.

Mediterranean Sea and warm Atlantic Ocean. Straits of Florida.

Fig. 333

Peridinium trochoideum (Stein) Lemmermann, 1910

Lemmermann, 1910, p. 336; Schiller, 1937, p. 137, fig. 134a-g; *Glenodinium trochoideum* Stein, 1883, pl. 3 (figs. 27-29).

Cell broadly pear-shaped; epitheca longer than hypotheca, margins convex, tapering into a small apical horn; girdle depressed, slightly or not offset; sulcus slight on epitheca, may or may not reach base; no antapicals. Length 15-35 μ.

Neritic in European waters. Bermuda; Gulf Stream (Hulburt, 1963).

Fig. 334

Peridinium tuba Schiller, 1937

Schiller, 1937, p. 273, fig. 278.

Body spherical with affixed and slightly flaring apical horn; girdle not displaced; lists narrow; sulcus wide, narrow lists ending in two long, thin spines; plates very indistinct. Length 20 μ.

Adriatic Sea. Straits of Florida.

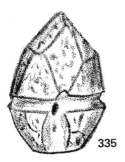

335

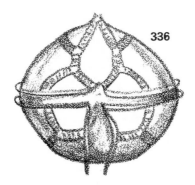

336

337

Fig. 335

Peridinium umbonatum Stein, 1883

Stein, 1883, pl. 12 (figs. 1-8); Wood, 1954, p. 233, fig. 104a-d.

Cell elongate-ovate, somewhat flattened dorsoventrally; epitheca larger than hypotheca, sides slightly angled, tapering to apex; hypotheca low, angular, base flat, spines absent; girdle depressed, straight; sulcus reaching base. Length 25-35 μ.

Cosmopolitan fresh-water species. Florida Everglades.

Fig. 336

Peridinium variegatum Peters, 1928

Peters, 1928, pl. 35 (fig. 9); Wood, 1954, p. 246, fig. 134a-b.

Body round to pyriform, right-handed; apical horn minute, arising from tapering epitheca; hypotheca round with two small spines, one an extension of left sulcal list. Length 50-90 μ.

Weddell Sea. Identified on three occasions in the Straits of Florida at temperatures up to 26° C.

Fig. 337

Peridinium volzii Lemmermann, 1905

Lemmermann, 1905, p. 166; Wood, 1954, p. 231, fig. 95.

Cell spherical, somewhat flattened ventrally; epitheca and hypotheca rounded, no spines, hypotheca smaller than epitheca; girdle depressed, slightly deflected; sulcus not reaching antapex. Length 36-60 μ.

Europe; Africa; Australia. Florida Everglades in fresh water.

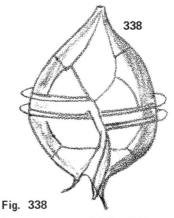

338

Fig. 338

Peridinium wiesneri Schiller, 1911

Schiller, 1911, p. 2, fig. 2; Schiller, 1937, p. 228, fig. 224a-e; Wood, 1954, p. 250, fig. 143.

Cell broadly rounded, apex and antapex tapering; apical horn conical; girdle left-handed, not depressed, lists present; sulcal lists ending in two more or less curved and unequal spines; tabulation meta, quadra. Length 55-70 μ.

Adriatic Sea; Atlantic Ocean; Australian east coast. Straits of Florida.

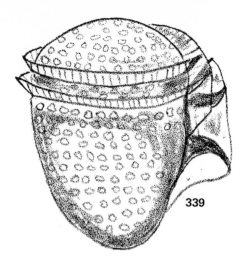

339

Genus PHALACROMA Stein

Body varying in shape with bilateral plates; epitheca usually rounded; hypotheca variable; girdle median or somewhat anterior with hyaline, often ribbed, transverse lists which do not extend above epitheca; left sulcal list moderately developed; protuberances and one or two spines may be present on hypotheca.

Fig. 339

Phalacroma acutum (Schütt) Pavillard, 1916

Pavillard, 1916, p. 55, pl. 3 (fig. 7); Wood, 1954, p. 188, fig. 22; *P. vastum* var. *acuta* Schütt, 1895, pl. 3 (fig. 17).

Body in lateral view asymmetrical, constricted laterally; epitheca high, rounded; hypotheca straight ventrally, rounded dorsally; girdle lists narrow, ribbed; right sulcal list reaching main rib, left widening below main rib, list extending posteriorly to R3, which is deflected posteriorly. Length 60-70 μ.

Mediterranean Sea; east Australia; Atlantic Ocean. Straits of Florida.

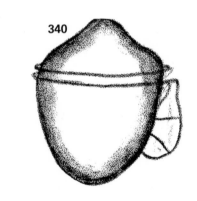

340

Fig. 340

Phalacroma apicatum Kofoid and Skogsberg, 1928

Kofoid and Skogsberg, 1928, p. 111, fig. 10.

Body in side view irregularly ovate to rhombic, in ventral view biconical with rounded ends, broadest at girdle; epitheca conical; lists narrow. Length 80-100 μ.

Tropical and subtropical Pacific Ocean. Brazil (north coast).

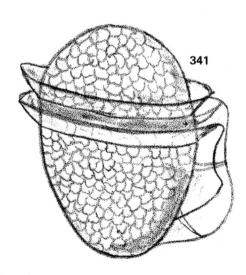

341

Fig. 341

Phalacroma argus Stein, 1883

Stein, 1883, pl. 18 (figs. 15-17); Wood, 1954, p. 186, fig. 16a-b.

Body oval in lateral view; epitheca high, about one-third body length; epitheca and hypotheca rounded, areolate; girdle lists may be ribbed; right sulcal list sinuate; left sulcal list rounded, widening towards base, R3 small; theca reticulate. Length 80-110 μ.

Tropical and subtropical waters of all oceans. Straits of Florida.

Fig. 342

Phalacroma biceps (Schiller) Schiller, 1933

Schiller, 1933, p. 71, fig. 65a; *Dinophysis biceps* Schiller, 1928, p. 75, fig. 37.

Body regularly oval, with two bulges in the top of the epitheca which characterize the species; anterior girdle list high, resembling that of a dinophysis; posterior list narrower than girdle; left sulcal list even, stopping just behind R3, which is about the middle of the ventral surface. Length 30-35 μ.

Adriatic Sea. Straits of Florida.

Fig. 342.1

Phalacrome bipartitum Kofoid and Skogsberg, 1928

Kofoid and Skogsberg, 1928, p. 166, fig. 21 (2).

Body in side view rotund; epitheca about one-quarter length of hypotheca; girdle narrow, lists narrow; left sulcal list narrow, widening to R3, then narrowing but continuous with two triangular processes, one posterior, the other somewhat dorsal, and supported by reticulate thickenings. Length 70 μ.

Eastern tropical Pacific Ocean. Straits of Florida.

Fig. 343

Phalacroma circumsutum Karsten, 1907

Karsten, 1907, p. 421, pl. 53 (fig. 8).

Body in lateral view oval, widest in middle; girdle anterior; epitheca rounded; R3 acute, ventral, supporting a sail which is connected narrowly with the left sulcal list and R2. Length 75-80 μ.

Tropical and warm waters. Brazil (north coast).

Fig. 344

Phalacroma cuneus Schütt, 1895

Schütt, 1895, p. 148, pl. 3, fig. 14; Wood, 1954, p. 187, fig. 20a-b.

Body cuneate with a low, broadly rounded epitheca; hypotheca cuneate, greatest width at girdle; girdle anterior, lists about girdle width; ribs at base of anterior list anastomose into one or two rows of polygons; posterior list simply ribbed; sulcus about half length of hypotheca, right sulcal list long and narrow, left sulcal list moderate, margin sigmoid, usually irregularly striate; theca reticulate. Length 70-90 μ.

Interoceanic, tropical and subtropical. Straits of Florida; Benguela Current.

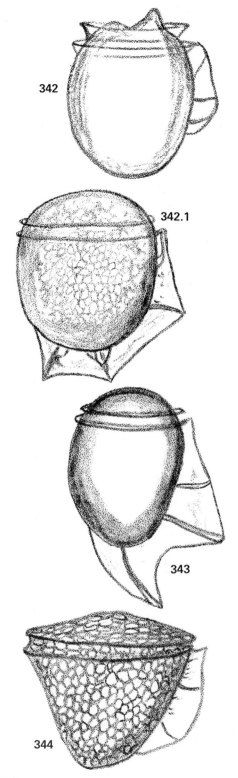

342

342.1

343

344

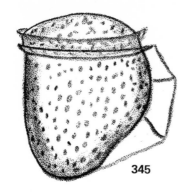

345

Fig. 345

Phalacroma dolichopterygium Murray and Whitting, 1899

Murray and Whitting, 1899, p. 330, pl. 31 (fig. 8a-b); Wood, 1954, p. 191, fig. 28a-c.

Epitheca low, conical with rounded apex; hypotheca rounded with longitudinal axis inclined ventrally and slight "bump" at base; girdle wider than lists; left sulcal list widening to R3, then tapering to theca margin. Length 50-80 μ.

East coast of Australia. Benguela Current; Brazil (north coast).

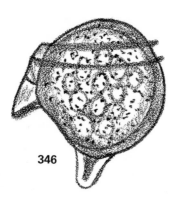

346

Fig. 346

Phalacroma doryphorum Stein, 1883

Stein, 1883, p. 23, pl. 19 (fig. 4); Wood, 1954, p. 191, fig. 30a-b.

Body in lateral view more or less oval, deepest at or behind girdle; epitheca evenly or moderately convex to flat, somewhat elevated above girdle; hypotheca oval or cuneate, narrower posteriorly; girdle flat or slightly convex, lists not spined; right sulcal list ends above posterior main rib, left sulcal list triangular, wide at posterior main rib; posterior sail with or without supporting rib, at or ventral to antapex; theca closely areolate. Length 50-90 μ.

Interoceanic warm waters. West Channel, Straits of Florida; Benguela Current; Brazil (north coast).

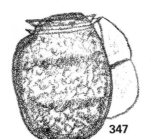

347

Fig. 347

Phalacroma expulsum (Kofoid and Michener) Kofoid and Skogsberg, 1928

Kofoid and Skogsberg, 1928, p. 157, pl. 5 (fig. 1); *Dinophysis expulsa* Kofoid and Michener, 1911, p. 268.

Epitheca low, slightly higher ventrally; girdle moderate, lists rather wide, anterior list wider than posterior; body somewhat constricted laterally; left sulcal list narrow, hyaline; R3 absent. Length 50-70 μ.

Tropical and subtropical waters. Straits of Florida.

Fig. 348

Phalacroma favus Kofoid and Michener, 1911

Kofoid and Michener, 1911, p. 289; Kofoid and Skogsberg, 1928, p. 146, pl. 2, fig. 7.

Body subcuneate in lateral view; epitheca very broadly rounded, shallow, lists heavily ribbed; posterior portion of hypotheca constricted, mammiliform, with ventral margin broadly rounded or somewhat angular at posterior main rib of left sulcal list; left sulcal list moderate to decurrent, strongly ribbed. Length 50-90 μ.

Tropical and subtropical waters. Brazil (north coast).

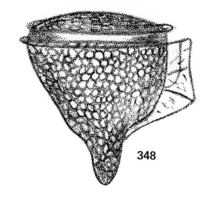

348

Fig. 349

Phalacroma hindmarchi Murray and Whitting, 1899

Murray and Whitting, 1899; Wood, 1954, p. 191, fig. 29.

Body an inverted-fig shape; epitheca broad, convex, low; hypotheca rounded with slightly capitate penducle at antapex, broadest at or behind girdle; girdle list not ribbed; right sulcal list extends to main rib of left sulcal list, which is widest at posterior main rib, tapering to base of peduncle. Length 80-100 μ.

Interoceanic in warm waters. Straits of Florida; Benguela Current; Brazil (north coast).

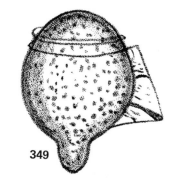

349

Fig. 350

Phalacroma mitra, Schütt, 1895

Schütt, 1895, pl. 4 (fig. 18); Wood, 1954, p. 89, fig. 26.

Possibly identical with *P. rapa.* Epitheca low; hypotheca with distinct process directed posteriorly on dorsal side, rounded; ventral contour more rounded than that of *P. rapa;* process more pronounced than in *P. dolichopterygium;* surface porulate; left sulcal list widening to R3 and extending beyond it, but strictly ventral. Length 70 μ.

Warm-water species, widely distributed. Straits of Florida.

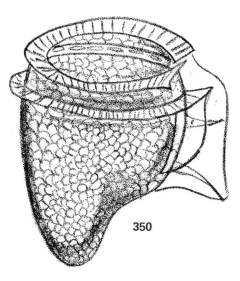

350

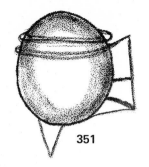

Fig. 351

Phalacroma mucronatum Kofoid and Skogsberg, 1928

Kofoid and Skogsberg, 1928, p. 172, pl. 22 (figs. 4, 6, 8); Wood, 1963*a*, p. 5, fig. 8.

Body in lateral view circular; girdle anterior; epitheca low, rounded; girdle lists shallow; hypotheca rotund, with an antapical spine; left sulcal list moderately wide, ending at R3. Length 35-45 μ.

Eastern tropical Pacific Ocean; Coral Sea. Straits of Florida.

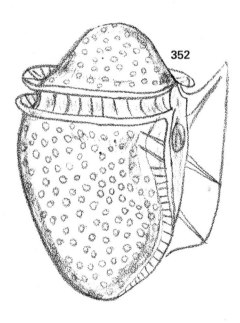

Fig. 352

Phalacroma operculatum Stein, 1883

Stein, 1883, pl. 18 (fig. 8); Schiller, 1933, p. 76, fig. 69; Wood, 1954, p. 185, fig. 14.

Body somewhat biconical; epitheca small but dome-shaped; hypotheca ovate with obtusely rounded base; girdle somewhat depressed, lists narrow, spined; left sulcal list of even width, extending beyond R3 but still ventral; surface porulate. Length 70-80 μ.

Atlantic Ocean, Mediterranean Sea, and Port Hacking (Australia); winter species. Straits of Florida.

Fig. 353

Phalacroma ovum Schütt, 1895

Schütt, 1895, p. 90; Wood, 1954, p. 186, fig. 17.

Body ovate, deepest at or behind girdle; epitheca prominent, usually very convex; hypotheca symmetrical or slightly inclined ventrally, posterior portion much narrower than anterior; girdle not depressed, lists without spines; left sulcal list narrow, widening posteriorly, straight or concave, sometimes sigmoid. Length 60-80 μ.

Santaren Channel, Straits of Florida; Benguela Current; Brazil (north coast).

Fig. 354

Phalacroma parvulum (Schütt) Jörgensen, 1923

Jörgensen, 1923, pp. 7, 8, 9, pl. 45 (fig. 4); Wood, 1963a, p. 6, fig. 10, *P. porodictyum* var. *parvula* Schütt, 1895, pl. 2 (fig. 13).

Body small, spherical to sphaeroidal, widest in the middle; left sulcal list almost triangular, about half body length. Length 35-60 μ.

Worldwide in warm waters. West Channel, Straits of Florida; Benguela Current; Gulf Stream (Hulburt, 1963).

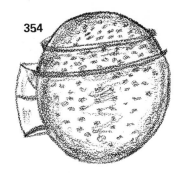

354

Fig. 355

Phalacroma porodictyum Stein, 1883

Stein, 1883, pl. 18, figs. 11-14; Schiller, 1937, p. 73, fig. 66a-b.

Body elliptical; epitheca high, about one-half height of hypotheca, round; hypotheca rotund; girdle even, lists narrow, even; right sulcal list rather large; left sulcal list widening toward R3, and extending beyond this rib but entirely ventral. Length 70-80 μ.

Tropical and subtropical seas. Straits of Florida.

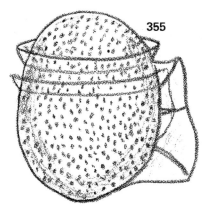

355

Fig. 356

Phalacroma pugiunculus Jörgensen, 1923

Jörgensen, 1923, p. 18, fig. 19; Schiller, 1933, p. 102, fig. 94.

Body ovate, rather flattened on apex; epitheca smaller than hypotheca; girdle slightly constricted, girdle lists moderate, basal spine present, median; left sulcal list even, margin straight, rectangular; R3 supporting angle of list. Length 50 μ.

Mediterranean Sea. Straits of Florida; Caribbean Sea.

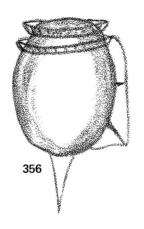

356

Fig. 357

Phalacroma pulchellum Lebour, 1925

Lebour, 1925, p. 77, pl. 11, fig. 2a-e; Wood, 1954, p. 184, fig. 9.

Body rotund, slightly flattened; epitheca evenly rounded; girdle broad, depressed, lists narrow, anterior; hypotheca rounded, widest in middle; sulcus extending into epitheca; left sulcal list small, about one-half length of hypotheca with spines. Length 20-40 μ.

Plymouth Sound; Port Hacking (Australia); Antarctic convergence. Gulf Stream (Hulburt, 1963); Brazil (north coast).

357

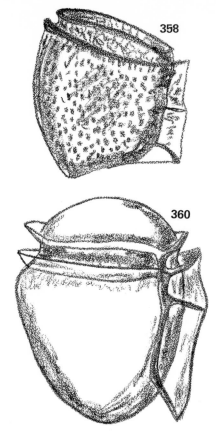

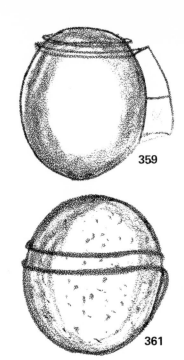

Fig. 358

Phalacroma rapa Stein, 1883

Stein, 1883, p. 23, pl. 19 (figs. 5, 8); Wood, 1954, p. 188, fig. 24a-b.

Body subcuneate in lateral view; epitheca moderately convex to flat; hypotheca narrowly rounded to subacute, ventral margin of hypotheca strikingly angular at main rib of left sulcal list, deepest at girdle; girdle lists ribbed; right sulcal list usually subtriangular. Length 70-100 μ.

Tropical and temperate waters, interoceanic. Straits of Florida; Tongue of the Ocean; Benguela Current.

Fig. 359

Phalacroma rotundatum (Claparède and Lachmann) Kofoid and Michener, 1911

Kofoid and Michener, 1911, p. 290; Schiller, 1933, p. 67, fig. 60a-d.

Body round, almost circular; epitheca low, evenly rounded; hypotheca evenly rounded; long axis verical; girdle not depressed, lists narrow; sulcal list even or slightly wider at R3, hyaline. Length 40-60 μ.

Widely distributed in Atlantic Ocean and its seas. Straits of Florida; Benguela Current; Gulf Stream (Hulburt, 1963); Brazil (north coast).

Fig. 360

Phalacroma rudgei Murray and Whitting, 1899

Murray and Whitting, 1899, p. 331, pl. 31 (fig. 6); Wood, 1954, p. 185, fig. 13a-b.

Body in side view almost circular to ovate; epitheca rounded, moderately high; girdle slightly depressed, girdle lists narrow; sulcal list somewhat narrow, even, ending at R3, which is definitely ventral. Length 75 μ.

Subtropical Atlantic and Pacific oceans. Straits of Florida.

Fig. 361

Phalacroma sphaeroideum Schiller, 1928

Schiller, 1928, p. 69, fig. 30a-c; Schiller, 1933, p. 82, fig. 74a-c.

Body rotund, almost spherical; epitheca lower than hypotheca; girdle wide, lists very narrow; sulcus lists also very narrow; surface with scattered pores. Length 25-30 μ.

Adriatic Sea. Straits of Florida.

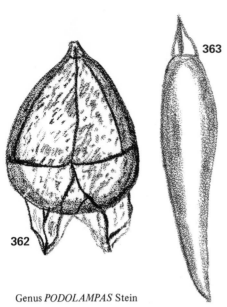

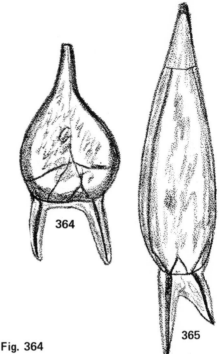

Genus *PODOLAMPAS* Stein

Cells pyriform, tapering to an apical horn often with a spine; girdle not apparent, probably fused with precingular plates; flagellar pore in ventral area; one to two strong antapical spines, one with wing fused to left sulcal list.

Fig. 362

Podolampas bipes Stein, 1883

Stein, 1883, pl. 8, figs. 6-8; Wood, 1954, p. 316, fig. 251a.

Cell broadly pear-shaped, narrowing to apical horn; girdle not apparent, probably fused with adjacent precingular plates; flagellar pore in ventral area; two strong, equal, antipical spines supporting transverse wings, the left being a continuation of the ventral area; theca porulate, wings more or less reticulate; plate formula 2', la 6'', 3''', 4''''. Length 80-100 μ.

Tropical, interoceanic species. West Channel, Straits of Florida; Benguela Current; Brazil (north coast); Caribbean Sea.

Fig. 363

Podolampas curvatus Schiller, 1937

Schiller, 1937, p. 476, fig. 549

Body narrow, tapering to an acute point at apex; apex bent to the right; antapex blunt with spine supporting broad wing. Length 30-40 μ.

Adriatic Sea; Coral Sea. Straits of Florida.

Fig. 364

Podolampas elegans Schütt, 1895

Schütt, 1895, p. 18, fig. 57; Wood, 1963a, p. 50, fig. 186.

Body pear-shaped, tapering into a tube-like apical horn and with two subequal antapical spines joined by a wing, which also extends on outer sides of spines. Length 25-100 μ.

Indian, Pacific, and Atlantic oceans in tropical and subtropical waters. Santaren Channel, Straits of Florida; Benguela Current; Gulf of Mexico (Curl, 1959); Brazil (north coast); Caribbean Sea.

Fig. 365

Podolampas palmipes Stein, 1883

Stein, 1883; Wood, 1954, p. 317, fig. 252a-b.

Cell elongate pear-shaped, narrow in front, gradually tapering to a slender apical horn; left antapical spine much longer than right, which may be absent; wings fused; transverse seam often broad. Length 7-110 μ.

We should probably unite *P. palmipes* and *P. spinifer* as they very frequently occur together, and gradations are very common.

Tropical interoceanic species. Santaren Channel, Straits of Florida; Benguela Current; Sargasso Sea (Hulburt, 1963); Brazil (north coast); Caribbean Sea.

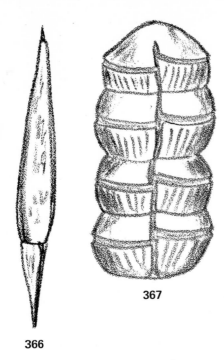

367

366

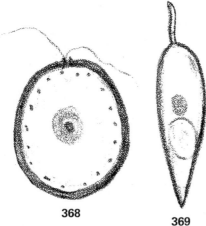

368

369

Fig. 366

Podolampas spinifer Okamura, 1912

Okamura, 1912, p. 17, pl. 2 (figs. 35-36); Schiller, 1937, p. 476, fig. 548.

Body elongate pear-shaped, tapering into an apical horn with a small apical spine; antapex rounded with a single spine supporting a wing. Length 90-120 μ.

Widely distributed in warmer waters. Straits of Florida; Caribbean Sea.

Genus *POLYKRIKOS* Bütschli

Cells occurring in chains, with incomplete separation of the cells; girdle depressed, left-handed, displaced about one width; sulcus extending onto apex of anterior cell, then straight and continuous to base of posterior cell.

Fig. 367

Polykrikos kofoidi Chatton, 1914

Chatton, 1914, p. 161; Kofoid and Swezy, 1921, p. 398, pl. 4 (fig. 47).

Chain of two to eight cells; epitheca smooth; hypotheca ribbed; girdle left-handed, displaced; sulcus continuous from near apex of leading cell. Length of each cell 25-45 μ.

Pacific Ocean. Bear Cut; Straits of Florida.

Genus *PORELLA* Schiller

Cell rounded to oval; plates as in *Exuviaella*, lateral plates strongly depressed in center; anterior may have minute, tooth-like processes.

Fig. 368

Porella perforata (Gran) Schiller, 1933

Schiller, 1933, p. 27, fig. 26a-c; Wood, 1954, p. 179, fig. 3; *Exuviaella perforata* Gran, 1915.

Cell rounded-oval, flattened laterally; cone-like indentation in each valve with a row of poroids around the margin; one valve with two pores borne on a small projection fitting a hollow in the other valve. Length 20-30 μ.

Straits of Florida; Benguela Current; Sargasso Sea (Hulburt *et al.,* 1960); Brazil (north coast).

Genus *PRONOCTILUCA* Fabre-Domérgue

Cell not thecate, with anterior tentacle and sulcus; girdle anterior and feebly developed; long transverse flagellum and short or long longitudinal flagellum.

Fig. 369

Pronoctiluca acuta (Lohmann) Schiller, 1933

Schiller, 1933, p. 271, fig. 260a; Wood, 1954, p. 217, fig. 76; *Rhynchomonas acuta* Lohmann, 1912, p. 245, fig. 17a.

Body fusiform, slender, broadest anteriorly, apex rounded, base tapering to a conical point; tentacle about one-quarter body length. Length 35 μ.

Widely distributed in oceanic waters. Caribbean Sea.

Fig. 370

Pronoctiluca pelagica Fabre-Domérgue, 1889

Fabre-Domérgue, 1889; Wood, 1954, p. 216, fig. 74.

Cell spindle- to pear-shaped; tentacle slender, terminal; girdle and sulcus anterior; both flagella long, one anterior, the other posterior; punctated membrane covering cell. Length 12-50 μ.

Cosmopolitan. Straits of Florida; east of Antilles (Hulburt, 1962); Brazil (north coast).

Fig. 371

Pronoctiluca spinifera (Lohmann) Schiller, 1933

Schiller, 1933, p. 27, fig. 259a-d; Wood, 1954, p. 217, fig. 75; *Rhynchomonas spinifer* Lohmann, 1920, pp. 216-217, fig. 63.

Body narrow, elongate, slightly asymmetrical, broadest toward base; apex asymmetrical with almost straight, parallel walls, usually ending in a short, blunt process; girdle, sulcus, and flagellar pores as in *P. pelagica*; tentacular process slender, cylindrical. Length 24-50 μ.

Cosmopolitan. Straits of Florida; Caribbean Sea.

Genus *PROROCENTRUM* Ehrenberg

Cell elongate-oval; anterior end bluntly pointed with spinous projection at pole; posterior end usually acute; theca consisting of two porulate plates united by a third, continuous plate; two anterior flagella.

Fig. 372

Prorocentrum arcuatum Issel, 1928

Issell, 1928, p. 278, fig. 2

Body in lateral view with angular dorsal margin, sharply bent near middle; ventral margin more rounded, convex anteriorly, then somewhat concave or straight; antapex acute; spine long, fine, winged. Length 70-80 μ.

Mediterranean Sea; Indian and Pacific oceans. Amazon delta.

Fig. 373

Prorocentrum cornutum Schiller, 1918

Schiller, 1918, p. 254, fig. 4; Schiller, 1933, p. 34, fig. 35a-b.

Theca ovate to circular with a blunt ant-

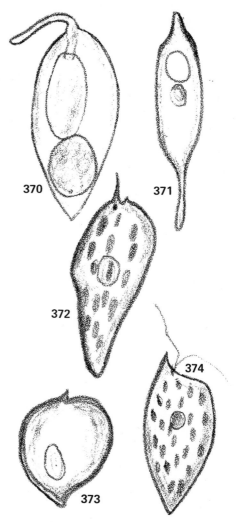

apical process; a small apical spine present. Length 16-29 μ.

Adriatic Sea. Straits of Florida.

Fig. 374

Prorocentrum dentatum Stein, 1883

Stein, 1883, pl. 1, figs. 14-15; Schiller, 1933, p. 43, fig. 46a-c.

Cell elongate-oval, broadest in the middle, tapering to an acute point antapically; both valves tapering into a single, toothed process at the ventral apex; surface porulate. Length 50-60 μ.

Atlantic Ocean and offshoots. Straits of Florida; Benguela Current; Sargasso Sea (Hulburt, 1963).

121

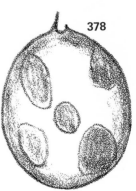

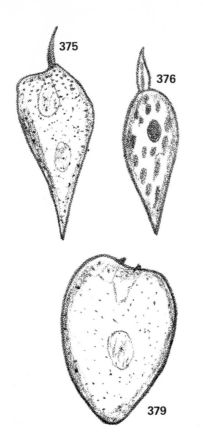

Fig. 375

Prorocentrum gibbosum Schiller, 1933

Schiller, 1933, p. 39, fig. 42a-b; *P. micans* var. *gibbosum* Schiller, 1929, p. 394, fig. 1.

Cell long, blunt in front, dorsally somewhat angular, tapering from about mid-line to antapex, which is acute, pointed; apical spine long and curved. Length 50-60 μ. This species, *P. arcuatum, P. schilleri,* and possibly *P. hentscheli* would appear to be forms of *P. micans.*

Mediterranean Sea; Indian and Pacific oceans. Straits of Florida.

Fig. 376

Prorocentrum gracile Schütt, 1895

Schütt, 1895, pl. 1 (fig. 3); Wood, 1963*b*, p. 3, fig. 3.

Body elongate, rounded anteriorly, widest about one-third of the distance from apex, posteriorly tapering; sides slightly concave with a long, sharp, slightly sigmoid process. Length 50-60 μ.

Atlantic Ocean; Coral Sea. Sargasso Sea (Hulburt, 1963); Brazil (north coast).

Fig. 377

Prorocentrum hentscheli Schiller, 1933

Schiller, 1933, p. 37, fig. 38a-b.

Cell generally similar to *P. micans* but slightly thinner and differing in the spear-pointed spine. Length 65 μ.

Tropical Atlantic Ocean (Meteor). Straits of Florida.

Fig. 378

Prorocentrum lebourae Schiller, 1928

Schiller, 1928, p. 33, fig. 34.

Body broadly elliptical, broadest in the middle, base round; surface with rows of pores; both valves with wings, the left with a long, sharp spine, the right with a small spur. Length 50 μ.

Adriatic Sea. Sargasso Sea (Hulburt, 1963); Gulf Stream; Caribbean Sea.

Fig. 379

Prorocentrum maximum Schiller, 1933

Schiller, 1933, p. 41, fig. 44a-c.

Body oval, dorsal lobe anterior to flagellar pore, ventral side rounded; antapex rounded, acute; theca porulate with coarse and fine pores; small spinelets without wing. Length 25 μ.

Adriatic Sea. Straits of Florida.

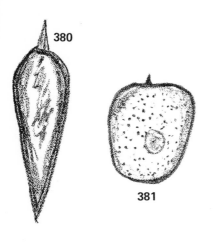

380

381

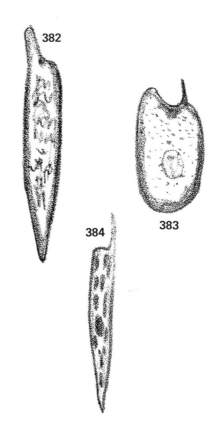

382

383

384

Fig. 380

Prorocentrum micans Ehrenberg, 1833

Ehrenberg, 1833, p. 307; Wood, 1954, p. 179, fig. 5.

Cells strongly compressed laterally, broadest about the middle, dorsally more convex than ventrally with a solid tooth and winglike membrane on left valve only; posterior spine reported by Gran and Braarud. Length 35-50 μ.

Cosmopolitan. West Channel, Santaren Channel, Straits of Florida; Benguela Current; Bermuda (Hulburt, 1963); Gulf Stream (Hulburt, 1963); Brazil (north coast); Caribbean Sea.

Fig. 381

Prorocentrum minimum Schiller, 1933

Schiller, 1933, p. 32, fig. 33a-b.

Body ovate, blunt ventrally, rounded dorsally; thickened at flagellar pores; pores numerous. Length 20 μ.

Mediterranean Sea; Aral Sea. Senix Creek; Sargasso Sea (Hulburt, 1963); Straits of Florida; Florida Everglades.

Fig. 382

Prorocentrum obtusidens Schiller, 1928

Schiller, 1928, p. 57, pl. 15; Wood, 1963a, p. 4, fig. 3.

Body subrotund with blunt apex, sides parallel then rounded to an acute antapex; process low, rounded. Length 40 μ.

Gulf Stream (Hulburt, 1963).

Fig. 383

Prorocentrum ovale (Gourret) Schiller, 1933

Schiller, 1933, p. 42, fig. 45; *Postprorocentrum ovale* Gourret, 1883, p. 83, pl. 1 (fig. 23).

Body somewhat elliptical, but with anterior portion protruding forward equal to or higher than the wingless spine, base evenly rounded. Length 25 μ.

Mediterranean Sea. Straits of Florida.

Fig. 384

Prorocentrum rostratum Stein, 1883

Stein, 1883, pl. 1, figs. 16-17; Wood, 1954, p. 181, fig. 7.

Cell elongate, about five to six times longer than broad; both valves ending in a long, thin process which in valve view is pointed, in suture view notched or flat; antapex very acute. Length 45-60 μ.

Warm-water species; Gulf Stream (Hulburt, 1962); Bermuda (Hulburt, 1963); Straits of Florida.

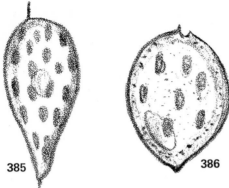

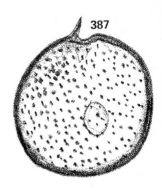

385 386

387

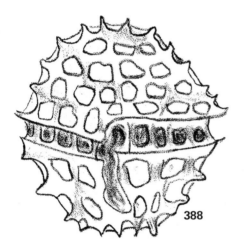

388

Fig. 385

Prorocentrum schilleri Bohm, 1933

Bohm, in Schiller, 1933, p. 38, fig. 40a-e.

Body in lateral view with rotund anterior and tapering posterior portion; valves may be unlike and one may have a posterior spine; anterior spine fine, winged or absent. Length 45-50 μ.

Adriatic Sea; Coral Sea region. Brazil (north coast).

Fig. 386

Prorocentrum scutellum Schröder, 1901

Schröder, 1901, pl. 1, fig. 12; Wood, 1954, p. 179, fig. 4.

Cell broadly heart-shaped, slightly indented in front, with distinct spine on left valve and an extremely thin wing; base slightly pointed

or rounded, porulate. Length 40-60 μ.

Interoceanic, neritic or estuarine. Common in Straits of Florida; Benguela Current; Gulf Stream (Hulburt, 1963); Brazil (north coast); Florida Everglades.

Fig. 387

Prorocentrum sphaeroideum Schiller, 1928

Schiller, 1928, p. 61, fig. 25a-b; Schiller, 1933, p. 32, fig. 31a-b.

Body flattened, circular in outline with thick theca, porulate; apical tooth with or without thin spine. Length 40-50 μ.

In Salps. Straits of Florida.

Genus *PROTOCERATIUM* Bergh

Cell spherical to subangular; girdle equatorial or subequatorial, depressed, even; sulcus not reaching base; surface of theca strongly reticulate obscuring plates; spines may be present at intersection of sutures; no apical horn; plate formula probably 2', 6'', 6''', 1 p, 1''''.

Fig. 388

Protoceratium areolatum Kofoid, 1907

Kofoid, 1907b, p. 169, pl. 12 (fig. 71).

Body roughly spherical; epitheca rounded; girdle recessed, submedian, strongly areolate; hypotheca subangular; sulcus short, depressed, rounded at base; theca surface very rugosely areolate; areolae coarse with blunt spinules between. Length 30-40 μ.

Pacific, Indian, and Atlantic oceans in warm waters. Straits of Florida; Caribbean region.

124

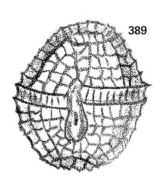

389

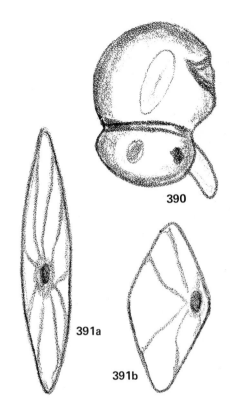

390

Fig. 389

Protoceratium reticulatum (Claparède and Lachmann) Bütschli, 1885

Bütschli, 1885, p. 1007, pl. 52 (fig. 2); Wood, 1954, p. 266, fig. 182; *Peridinium reticulatum* Claparède and Lachmann, 1858-1862, p. 20, fig. 3.

Body rotund; epitheca and hypotheca subequal, round or angular; girdle left-handed, displaced about one width; lists narrow, supported by spines; ventral area not reaching antapex; theca slightly reticulate, often with apicules; plates very difficult to see on account of reticulation. Length 30-50 μ.

Estuarine-neritic species. Benguela Current; Caribbean Sea.

Genus *PROTOERYTHROPSIS* Kofoid and Swezy

Body ellipsoid; girdle median, spiral; sulcus also spiral; stout prod or ventero-posterior process.

Fig. 390

Protoerythropsis crassicaudata Kofoid and Swezy, 1921

Kofoid and Swezy, 1921, p. 11, text fig. PP9, fig. 123.

Body ellipsoid; girdle a spiral of one and one-fifth turns; sulcus about three-fifths of a turn; stout ventero-posterior process. Length 70 μ.

California coast; east Coral Sea. Straits of Florida; Benguela Current.

391a

391b

Genus *PYROCYSTIS* Murray

Cell naked, very large and hyaline with chloroplasts held in protoplasmic threads radiating from nucleus to cell wall; spores multiple, gymnodinioid.

Fig. 391a-b

Pyrocystis fusiformis (W. Thomson) Murray, 1885

Murray, 1885, p. 937, fig. 338; Wood, 1954, p. 318, fig. 256a-b; W. Thomson, 1876.

a. Vegetative cells large, thin and fusiform or wider and shorter with rounded ends; protoplasmic strands marginal; spores gymnodinium-like. Length to 600 μ.

Interoceanic warm-water species. Straits of Florida; Benguela Current; Gulf Stream (Hulburt, 1963).

b. Var. *biconica* Kofoid, 1907b, p. 166.

Cells shorter and broader than type. Length to 400 μ.

Straits of Florida; Brazil (north coast).

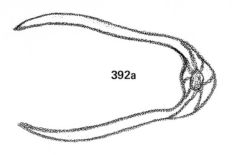

Fig. 392a

Pyrocystis hamulus Cleve, 1900

Cleve, 1900, p. 19, pl. f (fig. 23); Wood, 1954, p. 320, fig. 259a-b.

Cell body markedly swollen in the middle, with two thin, pointed arms variously curved and often twisted. 250 x 40 μ.

Tropical and subtropical waters; southwest Pacific Ocean. Straits of Florida.

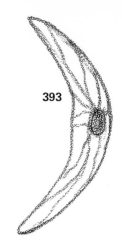

Fig. 393

Pyrocystis lunula Schütt, 1896

Schütt, 1896, pl. 3 (fig. 2b-f); Wood, 1954, p. 319, fig. 257a-b.

Cells large, lunate with tapering ends; protoplasm peripheral in strands; spherical cysts formed; swarm spores gymnodinioid. Length 2-8 μ.

West Channel, Santaren Channel, Straits of Florida; Benguela Current; Brazil (north coast); Caribbean Sea.

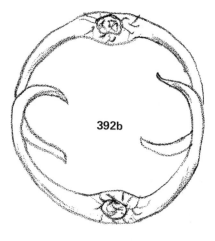

Fig. 392b

var. *semicircularis* Schröder, 1906

Pyrocystis hamulus var. *semicircularis* Schröder, 1906, p. 371, fig. 45.

Midbody ellipsoidal; arms almost semicircular, long and slender, sigmoid or sharply curved toward the ends.

Tropical and subtropical waters; Pacific, Indian, and Atlantic oceans. Straits of Florida.

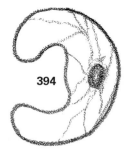

Fig. 394

Pyrocystis obtusa Pavillard, 1931

Pavillard, 1931, p. 38; Wood, 1963b, p. 18, fig. 61.

Body lunate with blunt ends directed toward each other. Length 150-250 μ.

East Indian Ocean. Sargasso Sea (Hulburt, 1963).

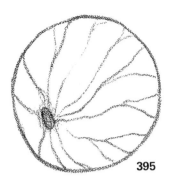

395

Fig. 395

Pyrocystis pseudonoctiluca W. Thomson, 1876

W. Thomson, 1876; Schiller, 1937, pp. 485-486, fig. 556a-c.

Cells spherical or elliptical; protoplast peripheral in strands, radiating from nucleus. Diameter 600-1,600 μ.

Interoceanic warm-water species. Benguela Current; Brazil (north coast).

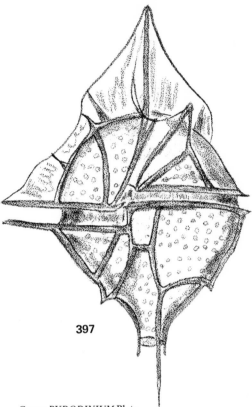

397

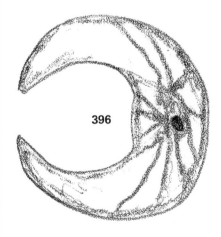

396

Fig. 396

Pyrocystis robusta Kofoid, 1907

Kofoid, 1907b, p. 167, pl. 1, fig. 5; Schiller, 1937, p. 492, fig. 568.

Body lunate with incurved extremities forming an almost complete circle; midbody wide. Length 500 μ.

Tropical and subtropical waters. Straits of Florida.

Genus *PYRODINIUM* Plate

Body roughly spherical; apical horn obvious, closed with a plate; epitheca and hypotheca equal; girdle displaced about one width with somewhat broad, hyaline lists; sulcal lists extending from above apex to a spine at base, widest at girdle and base.

Fig. 397

Pyrodinium bahamense Plate, 1906

Plate, 1906, p. 411, pl. 19; Schiller, 1937, p. 313, fig. 329a-c.

Body almost spherical with a wide apical horn and one large or two small spines; epitheca rounded or angular; hypotheca rounded; girdle depressed, with hyaline lists, displaced about one width; sulcus flaring to base with broad lists which extend onto a large spine at the basal end; a list extends from the girdle to this spine on the left and part way from the spine to the girdle on the right. Length 50-60 μ.

Bahamas (New Providence); Puerto Rico; Northwest and Northeast Providence channels, Straits of Florida.

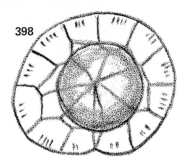

398

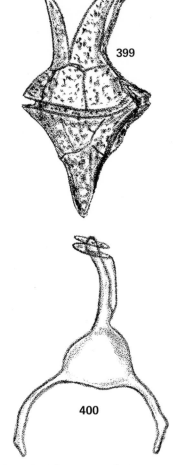

399

400

Genus *PYROPHACUS* Stein

Cell low, lenticular; epitheca and hypotheca equal, obliquely conical; girdle even; sulcus with a few small plates; plate formula 5', 9'', 9''', 3''''.

Fig. 398

Pyrophacus horologicum Stein, 1883

Stein, 1883, p. 24, figs. 8-13; Schiller, 1937 p. 87, fig. 73a-e.

Cell low, biconvex; lens-shaped test with epitheca and hypotheca equal, much wider than high; plates well marked with linear markings in the middle; sulcus with a few small plates; plate formula 5-7', 9-12'', 12-13''', 4-10''''. Length 40 μ.

Warm oceans. Brazil, only in Amazon delta.

Genus *SPIRAULAX* Kofoid

Differs from *Goniaulax* in that sulcus does not invade epitheca; theca is biconical with single antapical process. Often united with *Goniaulax*.

Fig. 399

Spiraulax jollifei (Murray and Whitting) Kofoid, 1911

Kofoid, 1911c; Wood, 1954, p. 265, fig. 181; *Goniaulax jollifei* Murray and Whitting, 1899, p. 324, pl. 28 (fig. 1a-b).

A stout species; body broadly and irregularly fusiform; epitheca and hypotheca subequal; subconical apex, truncate, margins concave; girdle displaced three widths, lists low; surface coarsely pitted; sulcus not invading epitheca; single strong antapical horn; plate formula 4, 1a, 6'', 6''', 1 p, 1''''. Length 200-400 μ.

Tropical oceanic, interoceanic. Santaren Channel, Straits of Florida; Brazil (north coast).

Genus *TRIPSOLENIA* Kofoid

Epitheca small, with very anterior girdle with small lists; sulcal lists not prominent; hypotheca with long neck and rotund body extending into two curved posterior processes which end in two slightly angled "feet."

Fig. 400

Triposolenia bicornis Kofoid, 1906

Kofoid, 1906, p. 96, pl. 15 (figs. 1-2).

Body subconical; epitheca rounded, low; neck elongate, angled dorsally; antapical horns evenly bent toward longitudinal axis, slightly rugose toward ends on outside. Length 150-200 μ.

Atlantic Ocean; Pacific Ocean; Mediterranean Sea. Brazil (north coast).

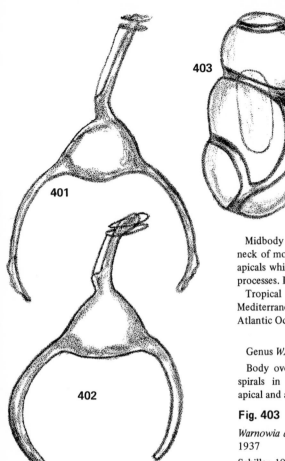

403

401

402

404

Fig. 401

Triposolenia intermedia Kofoid and Skogsberg, 1928

Kofoid and Skogsberg, 1928, p. 477, fig. 60, pl. 14 (fig. 10).

Body triangular with rotund sides; neck slender, about equal in length to antapicals which are more curved and closer to body; small processes on outer sides of antapicals. Length 165-180 μ.

Tropical and subtropical Pacific Ocean. Straits of Florida; Caribbean Sea.

Fig. 402

Triposolenia truncata Kofoid, 1906

Kofoid, 1906, p. 96, pl. 16 (fig. 5); Kofoid and Skogsberg, 1928, p. 463, fig. 62, pl. 14 (figs. 1-3).

Midbody rounded, triangular, sides convex; neck of moderate length, about equal to antapicals which are evenly curved and without processes. Length 110-150 μ.

Tropical and subtropical Pacific Ocean; Mediterranean Sea; Sea of Marmora; tropical Atlantic Ocean. Straits of Florida.

Genus *WARNOWIA* Lindemann

Body ovoid; girdle and sulcus descending spirals in opposite directions; sulcus has apical and antapical loops.

Fig. 403

Warnowia atra (Kofoid and Swezy) Schiller, 1937

Schiller, 1937, p. 565, fig. 595; Wood, 1963*a*, p. 35, fig. 124; *Pouchetia atra*, Kofoid and Swezy, 1921, p. 439.

Body ovoid; girdle a descending spiral of two and three-fifths turns; sulcus having two turns. Length 60-65 μ.

Tropical and subtropical Pacific Ocean. Benguela Current; Brazil (north coast).

Fig. 404

Warnowia violescens (Kofoid and Swezy) Lindemann, 1928

Lindemann, 1928, p. 52; Wood, 1963*a*, p. 36; *Pouchetia violescens* Kofoid and Swezy, 1921, p. 469, fig. 00 (b), pl. 6 (fig. 66).

Body ovoid; girdle spiral of one and four-fifths turns; sulcus with three turns and apical and antapical loops. Length 50-60 μ.

Warm Pacific waters. Benguela Current; Brazil (north coast).

APPENDIX

Silicoflagellates of the Caribbean Area

Six species of silicoflagellates have been recorded from the Caribbean area. These flagellates have an internal siliceous skeleton and the protoplast is very delicate. The addition of even 2 percent formalin usually results in the collapse of the protoplast, so the frequency of living organisms can be determined only by examination of fresh phytoplankton.

The organisms are widely distributed but are usually unimportant in numbers, although they were apparently very important in some areas in previous eras and are common in the fossil record. On one occasion *Distephanus speculum* was dominant in the Peril Strait-Sitka Sound area in Alaskan waters.

Genus *DICTYOCHA* Ehrenberg

Skeleton with a basal ring, and a convex portion which joins the centers of the sectors of this basal ring, which may be elliptical, or triangular, or more or less diamond-shaped. The convex portion may therefore be a curved strip, or have three or four rays. There are usually but not always spines extending outward from the corners.

(Hulburt, 1963); Gulf of Mexico (Curl, 1959); Tongue of the Ocean; East and West Providence channels, Santaren Channel, and West Channel, Straits of Florida; frequent but not abundant, Brazil (north coast); Caribbean Sea.

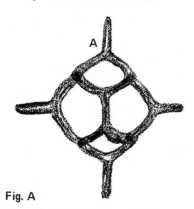

Fig. A

Dictyocha fibula Ehrenberg, 1859

Dictyocha fibula Ehrenberg, 1859, pl. 18 (figs. 54-55); Lemmermann, 1903, fig. 92.

Skeleton box-shaped; basal ring quadrate, rhombic or rhomboid with spines at corners and spinules or teeth along the limbs of the skeleton. Length 50-70 μ.

Cosmopolitan, living or fossil. Gulf Stream

Fig. B

Dictyocha navicula Ehrenberg, 1838

Ehrenberg, 1838, pl. 20 (fig. 43); Gemeinhardt, 1930, pp. 36-38, figs. 22-27.

Skeleton elongate-elliptical, smooth or with spines at ends and a semicircular bridge in the middle. Length 80-100 μ.

Fossil and present in plankton; not common. Straits of Florida; Caribbean Sea.

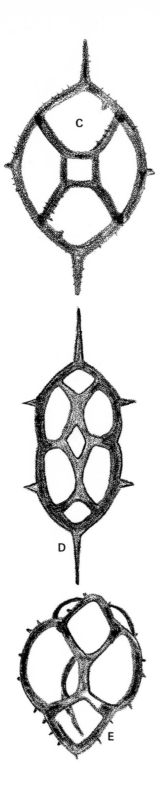

Genus *DISTEPHANUS* Haeckel

Skeleton with basal and apical rings, joined by four or six rays. Basal and apical rings may have four to a number of spines projecting outward and sometimes inward.

Fig. C

Distephanus crux (Ehrenberg) Haeckel, 1890

Haeckel, 1890; Gemeinhardt, 1930, p. 58, figs. 50-52.

Basal ring of skeleton quadrate, joined by four rays to quadrate apical ring; two or more spines extending outward from basal ring, none on apical ring. Length 20-50 μ.

Fossil, recent and present-day phytoplankton. Straits of Florida.

Fig. D

Distephanus speculum (Ehrenberg) Haeckel, 1889

Haeckel, 1889; Lemmermann, 1903, figs. 99, 101-102; *Dictyocha speculum* Ehrenberg, 1837, pl. 18, figs. 5-7, 19 (41), 21 (44b), 22 (48), 25 (47).

Basal ring hexagonal with two to six long spines at the corners; secondary structure varying in complexity, often with in-pointed spines or teeth. Length 50-70 μ. Often united with *Dictyocha*.

Cosmopolitan, living or fossil. Gulf Stream (Hulburt, 1963); Bermuda (Hulburt and Rodman, 1963); Straits of Florida (Hulburt and Rodman, 1963); Brazil (north coast.)

Genus *EBRIA* Borgert

Skeleton plano-convex with many large or small windows forming an irregular pattern.

Fig. E

Ebria tripartita (Schumann) Lemmermann, 1899

Lemmermann, 1899; Lemmermann, 1903, fig. 108; *Dictyocha tripartita* Schumann, 1867, pl. 1 (fig. 28).

Skeleton very variable, plano-convex with several larger or smaller windows; edges of skeleton with few or many teeth or spines. Diameter 40 μ.

Cosmopolitan, living and fossil. Gulf Stream south of 34° N. (Hulburt, 1963); Gulf of Mexico (Curl, 1959); Straits of Florida; Brazil (north coast); Caribbean Sea.

Genus *MESOCENA* Ehrenberg

Skeleton forming a ring in one plane.

Fig. F

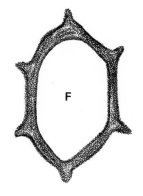

Mesocena polymorpha Lemmermann, 1901

Lemmermann, 1901, pl. 21 (figs. 3-10); Gemeinhardt, 1930, pp. 27-33, figs. 12-17.

Skeleton triangular to polygonal with spines at the corners, otherwise smooth or with spinules; flat, with hollow center. Length 20-60 μ.

Cosmopolitan but infrequent. Straits of Florida; Caribbean Sea; Gulf of Panama.

BIBLIOGRAPHY

Abé, T. H. 1927. Notes on the protozoan fauna of Mutsu Bay; Peridiniales. *Sci. Repts. Tohoku Univ.* 2, 639.

Bailey, J. W. 1855. Notes on new species and localities of microscopical organisms. Smithsonian Contrib. No. 7.

Bergh, R. S. 1881. Bidrag til Cilioflagellaternes Naturhistorie. *Nat. Vidensk. Medd, Copenhagen.* 60-76.

Bergh, R. S. 1882. Über die systematische Stellung der Gattung *Amphidinium. Zool. Anz.* 5, 12-16.

Bütschli, O. 1885. Dinoflagellata, in Protozoa (1880-1889), in Bronn, *Klass. u. Ordn. des Tierreichs.* 1, 906-1029.

Chatton, E. 1914. L'autogénèse des nématocystes chez *Polykrikos. C. R. Acad. Sci. Paris.* 158, 344.

Cienkowski, L. 1881. Bericht über eine Exkursion ins Weisse Meer im Jahre 1880. *Trav. Soc. Imp. Nat. St. Petersburg.* 11.1.

Claparède, E., and J. Lachmann. 1858-1861. Études sur les infusoires et les rhizopodes. *Mem. Inst. Génévois.* 5 (3), 1-260; 6, 261-482; 7, 1-291.

Cleve, P. T. 1899. Plankton collected by the Swedish expedition to Spitzbergen, in 1898. *K. Svenska Vetensk-Akad. Handl.* 32 (3), 51 pp.

Cleve, P. T. 1900. Notes on some Atlantic plankton organisms. *K. Svenska Vetensk-Akad. Handl.* 34 (1), 22 pp.

Cleve, P. T. 1901. Plankton from the Indian Ocean and the Malay Archipelago. *K. Svenska Vetensk-Akad. Handl.* 35 (5).

Conrad, W. 1926. Recherches sur les flagéllates de nos eaux saumatres. I. Dinoflagéllates. *Arch. Protist.* 55, 63.

Conrad, W. 1927. Recherches sur les flagéllates de nos eaux saumatres. II. Dinoflagéllates. *Arch. Protist.* 56.

Curl, H., Jr. 1959. The phytoplankton of Apalachee Bay and the Northeastern Gulf of Mexico. *Publ. Inst. Mar. Sci. U.of Texas.* 6, 277-320.

Dangeard, P. 1927. Péridiniens nouveaux ou peu connus de la croisière du *Sylvana. Bull. Inst. Oceanog. Monaco.*

Davis, C. C. 1948. A new species of *Gymnodinium. Bot. Gaz.* 109, 3.

Diesing, K. M. 1866. Revision der Prothelminthen. *S-B. Akad. Wissensch.Wien,* Math-nat. Kl. 52, 287.

Dogiel, V. 1906. Beitrag zur Kenntnis der Peridineen. *Mittel. Zool. Sta. Neapel.* 18, 1-45.

Dujardin, F. 1841. Histoire naturelle des Zoophytes, in *Suites à Buffon.* 684 pp.

Ehrenberg, C. G. 1833. Organisation in der Richtung des kleinsten Raumes. *Abh. Akad. Wissensch. Berlin.* 145-336.

Ehrenberg, G. C. 1838. Über die Bildung der Kreidefelsens und der Kreidemergels durch unsichtbare Organismen. *Abh. Akad. Wissensch. Berlin.* 67.

Ehrenberg, C. G. 1840. Über noch jetzt zahlreich lebende Tierarten der Kreidebildung und den Organismus der Polythalamien. *Abh. Akad. Widdensch. Berlin,* 1839. 81-174.

Ehrenberg, C. G. 1859. Über das Leuchten und über neue microscopische Leuchttiere des Mittelmeeres. *Mber. Berlin Akad. Wissensch,* 1859.

Entz, G., Jr. 1904. Die Fauna der kontinentalen Kochsalzwasser. *Math-Nat. Ber. Ungarn.* 18, 89-124.

Fabre-Domérgue. 1889. Note sur une nouvelle forme de Colpode et sur un flagéllate pélagique. *Ann. Micrographie.* 1.

135

Geitler, L. 1924. *Gymnodinium amphidinioides*, eine neue blaugrune Peridinee. *Bot. Arch.* 110.

Gemenihardt, K. 1930. *Silicoflagellates* in Dr. L. Rabenhorst's Kryptogamenflora von Deutschland, Österreich und der Schweiz. 10 (2), 1-87.

Gourret, P. 1883. Sur les péridiniens du Golfe de Marseille. *Ann. Mus. Nat. Hist. Marseille, Zool.* 1, 1-144.

Gräf, D. R. 1909. Biologie in *Planetforschungsreise,* 1906-1907. 4, 1-198.

Graham, H. W., and N. Bronikowsky. 1944. The Genus *Ceratium* in the Pacific and North Atlantic Oceans. Carnegie Inst. Publ. Biol. 5, 205 pp. Publ. No. 565.

Gran, H. H. 1902. Das Plankton des Norwegischen Nordmeeres vom biologischen und hydrographischen Gesichtpunkt behandelt. Rept. Norwegian Fish. Mar. Invest. 2 (5), 222 pp.

Gran, H. H. 1915. The plankton production in North European waters in the spring of 1912. *Cons. Intern. Perm. Expl. Mer, Bull.* Plankton. 1-142.

Haeckel, E. 1889. Report on radiolaria collected by H.M.S. Challenger. *Zool.* 18.

Haeckel, E. 1890. *Planktonstudien.* Jena.

Herdman, E. C. 1924. Notes on dinoflagellates and other organisms causing discoloration of the sand at Port Erin. *Trans. Liverpool Biol. Soc.* 37, 58-63; 38, 75-84.

Hulburt, E. M. 1957. The taxonomy of unarmored Dinophyceae of shallow embayments of Cape Cod, Mass. *Biol. Bull.* 112, 196-219.

Hulburt, E. M. 1962. Phytoplankton in the southwestern Sargasso Sea and North Equatorial current. *Limnol. Oceanog.* 7, 307-315.

Hulburt, E. M. 1963. Distribution of phytoplankton in coastal waters of Venezuela. *Ecology.* 44, 169-171.

Hulburt, E. M., and J. Rodman. 1963. Distribution of phytoplankton species with respect to salinity between the coast of southern New England and Bermuda. *Limnol. Oceanog.* 8, 263-269.

Hulburt, E. M., J. H. Ryther, and R. R. L. Guillard. 1960. The phytoplankton of the Sargasso Sea off Bermuda. *J. Cons. Perm. Int. Expl. Mer.* 25, 115-128.

Issel, R. 1928. Le variazioni del plancton nelle acque di Rovigno e.i. problem relative al plancton adriatico. Mem. R. Com. Talass. Italiano. 88, 1-26.

Jörgensen, E. 1899. Protophyten und Protozoen im Plankton aus der norwegischen Westküste. *Bergens Mus. Arb.* No. 6.

Jörgensen, E. 1911. Die Ceratien. Eine kurze Monographie der Gattung *Ceratium* Schrank. *Intern. Rev. ges Hydrob. u. Hydrog.* 4, Supp. 1, 124 pp.

Jörgensen, E. 1920. Mediterranean Ceratia. Rept. Danish Oceanog. Exped. 1908-1910. 2, J. 1. Biology 1.

Jörgensen, E. 1923. Mediterranean Dinophysiaceae. Rept. Danish Oceanog. Exped. 1908-1910. 2, J. 2.

Karsten, G. 1906. Das Plytoplankton des Atlantischen Ozeans, nach dem Material der deutschen Tiefsee Exped. *Valdivia.* 2 (2), Pt. 2, 137-209.

Karsten, G. 1907. Das indische Phytoplankton. Erg. Tiefsee Exp. *Valdivia.* 2, 221-548.

Kimball, J. F., Jr., and E. J. F. Wood. 1965. A Dinoflagellate with the characters of *Gymnodinium* and *Gyrodinium. J. Protozool.* 12, 577-580.

Klebs, G. 1912. Über Flagellaten und algenähnliche Peridineen. *Verh. Naturmed. Ver. Heidelberg.* 11, 367-451.

Kofoid, C. A. 1906. Dinoflagellata of the San Diego region, I. On *Heterodinium,* a new genus of the Peridineaceae. *Univ. Calif. Publ. Zool.* 2, 341.

Kofoid, C. A. 1907a. Dinoflagellata of the San Diego region, III. Descriptions of new species. *Univ. Calif. Publ. Zool.* 3, 299-340.

Kofoid, C. A. 1907b. Reports on the Agassiz Expedition, IX. New species of dinoflagellates. *Bull. Mus. Comp. Zool. Harvard College.* 50, 161-207.

Kofoid, C. A. 1908. Notes on some obscure species of *Ceratium. Univ. Calif. Publ. Zool.* 4 (7).

Kofoid, C. A. 1910. A Revision of the genus *Ceratocorys* based on skeletal morphology. *Univ. Calif. Publ. Zool.* 6, 177-187.

Kofoid, C. A. 1911a. Dinoflagellata of the San Diego region, IV. The genus *Gonyaulax* with notes on the skeletal morphology. *Univ. Calif. Publ. Zool.* 8, 187-300.

Kofoid, C. A. 1911b. Dinoflagellates of the San Diego region, V. *Univ. Calif. Publ. Zool.* 8, 295.

Kofoid, C. A. 1931. Rept. of the Biol. Survey of Mutsu Bay, 18. Protozoans, Subcl. Dinoflagellata. *Sci. Repts. Tohoku Univ.* Ser. 4.

Kofoid, C. A., and A. M. Adamson. 1933. The Dinoflagellatae; the family Heterodiniidae of the Peridinioideae. *Mem. Mus. Comp. Zool. Harvard College.* No. 54.

Kofoid, C. A., and E. Michener. 1911. Reports of the scientific results of the expedition to the eastern tropical Pacific in charge of Alexander Agassiz, 22. New genera and species of Dinoflagellates. *Bull. Mus. Comp. Zool. Harvard College.* 54, 265.

Kofoid, C. A., and T. Skogsberg. 1928. Dinoflagellatae; the Dinophysidae. *Mem. Mus. Comp. Zool. Harvard College.* No. 51.

Kofoid, C. A., and O. Swezy. 1921. The free-living unarmored Dinoflagellates. *Mem. Univ. Calif.* No. 5.

Lebour, M. V. 1922. Plymouth Peridineans, I-III. *J. Mar. Biol. Ass. U. K.* 12, 817-818.

Lebour, M. V. 1925. *The Dinoflagellates of northern seas.* Plymouth Marine Biol. Lab. 172 pp.

Lemmermann, E. 1899. Planktonalgen; Ergebnisse einer Reise nach dem Pacific. *Abh. Naturw. Ver. Bremen.* 16, 313-398.

Lemmermann, E., 1900. Planktonalgen. Ergebn. einer Reise nach dem Pazifik. *Abh. Naturw. Ver. Bremen.* 16.

Lemmermann, E. 1901. Das Phytoplankton des Ryck und der Greifs. Boddens. *Ber. Deutsch. Bot. Ges.* 1901.

Lemmermann, E. 1903. Das Phytoplankton des Meeres, II. *Abh. Natur. Ver. Bremen.* 17, 25.

Lemmermann, E. 1905. Das Phytoplankton des Meeres. *Bot. Zbl. Jena.* 19, 1-74.

Lemmermann, E. 1910. Planktonalgen aus dem Schliersee. *Arch. Hydrobiol.* 5.

Lohmann, H. 1902. Neue Untersuchungen über den Reichtum des Meeres an Plankton und über die Brauchbarkeit der verschiedenen Fang-Methoden. *Wiss. Meeresunter. Kiel.* 7, 1-86.

Lohmann, H. 1908. Untersuchungen zur Feststellung des vollständigen Gehaltes des Meeres an Plankton. *Wiss. Meeresunter. Kiel.* 10, 129-370.

Lohmann, H. 1920. Die Bevölkerung des Ozeans mit Plankton, nach dem Zentrifugen fange während der Ausreise der *Deutschland,* 1911. *Arch. Biont.* 4 (3), 1-617.

Mangin, L. 1926. *Phytoplancton antarctique.* Expéd. antarc. de la Scotia (1902-1904), 1.

Matzenauer, L. 1933. Die Dinoflagellaten des Indischen Ozeans. *Bot. Arch.* 35, 437-510.

Meunier, A. 1910. *Microplancton des mers de Barents et de Kara: Duc d'Orléans' campagne arctique de 1907.* Brussels: Bulens.

Meunier, A. 1919. Microplancton de la mer flamande. III. *Mem. Mus. Roy. Hist. Nat. Belgique.* 8, 1-116.

Moreira, H. 1964. Contribucio ao estudo das Diatomaceas da ragiao de cabo frio. *Boll. Univ. Parana. Bot.* 14. 11 pp.

Müller, O. F. 1773. *Vermium terrestrium et fluviatilum.* Haunias, Faber. 1 (30), 135 pp.

Murray, J. 1876. Preliminary reports to Prof. Wyville Thomson. *Proc. Roy. Soc. Lond.* 24, 471.

Murray, J. 1885. *Pyrocystis noctiluca.* Rep. Sci. Res. Challenger, Exp. Narrative. 1, Pt. 2, 935.

Murray, J., and F. Whitting. 1899. New Peridiniaceae from the Atlantic. *Trans. Linn. Soc. London.* (2) Bot., 5, 321.

Nitzsch, C. L. 1817. *Neue Schriften der Naturforschung.* Ges. zu Halle III. 1.

Okamura, K. 1912. Plankton organisms from bonito fishing grounds. *Rep. Imp. Bur. Fish. Jap.* No. 1.

Ostenfeld, C. H. 1899. *Plankton in 1898.* Kjöbenhavn: Gad.

Ostenfeld, C. H. 1906. Catalogue des espèces de plantes, et d'animaux, etc. Cons. Int.Perm. Expl. Mer. Publ. Circ. 33, 1-122.

Ostenfeld, C. H., and J. Schmidt. 1901. Plankton fra det Rode Hav of Adenbugten. *Medd. Naturh. Foren.* Kjöbenhavn. 141.

Paulsen, O. 1904. Plankton investigations in the waters around Iceland in 1903. *Medd. Komm. Havundersög.* 1, 1.

Paulsen, O. 1905. On some Peridineae and plankton diatoms. *Medd. Komm. Havundersög.* 1, 3.

Paulsen, O. 1907. The Peridiniales of the Danish waters. *Medd. Komm. Havundersög.* Plankton. 1, 1-26.

Paulsen, O. 1908. Peridiniales. *Nordisches Plankton*. Kiel: Brandt & Apstein.

Paulsen, O. 1930. Trabajos. Études sur le microplancton de la mer d'Alboran. *Min. Fomento Inst. Espan. Oceanogr.* 4.

Paulsen, O. 1949. Observations on Dinoflagellates. *Dansk. Vidensk. Akad. Selsk.* 6 (4), 1.

Pavillard, J. 1905. Recherches sur la flore pélagique (phytoplancton) de l'étang de Thau. *Mem. Univ. Montpellier*. Mxt. 2, i-116.

Pavillard, J. 1907. Sur les Ceratium du Golfe de Lyon. *Bull. Soc. Bot. France*, 54.

Pavillard, J. 1909. Sur les Péridiniens du Golfe de Lyon. *Bull. Soc. Bot. France*, 9, Ser. 4, 277.

Pavillard, J. 1916. Recherches sur les péridiniens du Golfe de Lyon. *Trav. Inst. Bot. Univ. Montpellier*. Mxt. mem. 4, 9-70.

Pavillard, J. 1923. À propos de la systematique des péridiniens. *Bull. Soc. Bot. France*. 70, 876-882.

Pavillard, J. 1930. Sur quelques formes intéressantes ou nouvelles du phytoplancton des croisières du Prince Albert 1er de Monaco. *Bull. Inst. Oceanog. Monaco*. 558.

Pavillard, J. 1931. Phytoplancton provenant des campagnes scientifiques du Prince Albert 1er de Monaco. Résultat des campagnes scientifiques. 82, 1-200.

Penard, E. 1891. Contributions à l'étude des Dinoflagelles. Recherches sur le *Ceratium macroceros*. Inaug. Diss. Genève. 34 pp.

Peters, N. 1928. Beitrag zur Planktonbevölkerung der Weddelsee. III. *Intern. Rev. ges. Hydrob. u. Hydrog.* 21, 18.

Plate, L. 1906. *Pyrodinium bahamense*, n. g., n. sp. Die Leuchtperidinee des Feuersees von Nassau, Bahama I. *Arch. Protist.* 7.

Pouchet, G. 1883. Contribution à l'histoire des cilio-flagelles, *J. Anat. Physiol.* 19, 399.

Pouchet, G. 1887. Quatrième contribution à l'histoire des Péridiniens. *J. Anat. Physiol.* 23, 87.

Saville-Kent, W. 1880-1882. *A Manual of Infusoria*. London: Bogue 1, 2.

Schiller, J. 1911. Neue *Peridinium* Arten aus der nördlichen Adria. *Osterr. Bot. Z.* No. 61.

Schiller, J. 1918. Über neue *Prorocentrum* u. *Exuviallea*-Arten. *Arch. Protist.* 38, 250.

Schiller, J. 1928. Die planktischen Vegetationen des Adriatischen Meeres. *Arch. Protist.* 61, 45; 62, 119.

Schiller, J. 1933. *Dinoflagellatae* in Dr. L. Rabenhorst's Kryptogamenflora von Deutschland, Österreich und der Schweiz. 10 (3), Pt. 1.

Schiller, J. 1937. *Dinoflagellatae* in Dr. L. Rabenhorst's Kryptogamenflora von Deutschland, Österreich und der Schweiz. 10 (3), Pt. 2.

Schmidt, A. 1875- . *Atlas der Diatomaceenkunde*. Leipzig: Reisland.

Schröder, B. 1906. Beiträge zur Kenntnis des Phytoplanktons warmer Meere. *Vjschr. naturf. Ges. Zürich*. 51, 319-377.

Schröder, B. 1911. Adriatisches Phytoplankton. *S-Ber. Akad. Wiss. Wien, Math. Nat. Kl.* 120, 501.

Schumann, J. 1867. *Preussiche Diatomeen*, II. Schr. Physoekon. Ges. Königsberg, 1867.

Schütt, F. 1893. Das Pfanzenleben der Hochsee, Ergeb. Planktonexp. 1, A. 243.

Schütt, F. 1895. Peridineen der Plankton-Expedition. Ergebn. Plankton-Exped. Humboldt-Stiftung. 4, 1-170.

Schütt, F. 1896. Peridiniales, in Engler u. Prantl, *Die Natürlichen Pflanzenfamilien*. Leipzig; Engelmann, I. B.

Schütt, F. 1900. Die Erklärung des centrifugalen Dickenwachstums der Membran. *Botan. Ztg.* 58, 245.

Stein, F. 1883. *Der Organismus der Flagellaten nach eigenen Forschungen in systematischer Reihenfolge bearbeitet*. III. 1, 1-154; 2, 30.

Vanhöffen, E. 1897. Fauna und Flora Grönlands. Grönland-Exped. Gessel. Erdkunde Berlin. 2, 254.

Woloszynska, J. 1916. Polnische Süsswasser Peridineen. *Bull. Acad. Sci. Crakovie Math-u. Nat.* Ser. B.

Wood, E. J. F. 1954. Dinoflagellates in the Australian region. *Aust. J. Mar. Fresw. Res.* 5, 171-351.

Wood, E. J. F. 1963a. Dinoflagellates in the Australian region. II. C.S.I.R.O. Div. Fish. Oceanog. Tech. Pap. 14, 55 pp.

Wood, E. J. F. 1963b. Dinoflagellates in the Australian region. III. C.S.I.R.O. Div. Fish. Oceanog. Tech. Pap. 17, 20 pp.

Wulff, A. 1916. Über das Kleinplankton der Barentssee. *Wiss. Meeresunters. Kiel*, N. S. Helgoland. I.

Zacharias, O. 1906. Das Plankton als Gegenstand eines zeitgemässen biologischen Schulunterrichts. *Arch. Hydrobiol.* (Plankt.) 1, 245.

LIST OF DINOFLAGELLATE SPECIES AND INDEX